# PRACTICE IN ENGLISH

# M. POSNER

# Practice in English

Test Papers for Foreign Students

**NELSON**

Thomas Nelson and Sons Ltd
Lincoln Way Windmill Road
Sunbury-on-Thames Middlesex TW16 7HP
P.O. Box 73146 Nairobi Kenya
P.O. Box 943
95 Church Street Kingston 5 Jamaica

Thomas Nelson (Australia) Ltd
19-39 Jeffcott Street West Melbourne Victoria 3003

Thomas Nelson and Sons (Canada) Ltd
81 Curlew Drive Don Mills Ontario

Thomas Nelson (Nigeria) Ltd
8 Ilupeju Bypass PMB 1303 Ikeja Lagos

© M. Posner 1971
First published 1971
Reprinted 1974 (twice) 1975, 1976, 1978

0 17 555059 X

Printed in Hong Kong

# CONTENTS

# CONTENTS

# TO THE TEACHER

This is a revision text for students at an intermediate, or fairly advanced level. The principal aim is to reinforce the grammatical points and linguistic structures that have already been taught, but have not been fully absorbed.

This is not a grammar book as such, but is meant to serve as a useful supplementary workbook to any existing intermediate or fairly advanced course. No matter what text is being used, most teachers will welcome additional practical exercises to help the student gain proficiency in the use of the basic forms.

The continual revision of important structures is, at this level, far more effective than ploughing through twenty to thirty sentences dealing with one particular structure and then neglecting to return to it systematically. Most of the exercises are therefore short (10–12 sentences), thus ensuring constant repetition throughout the book.

Nearly all the exercises, particularly the tense paragraphs, can – and should – be repeated at certain intervals during the course. It is consequently important to forbid the student to write down the correct answers in his copy of the book. Any weakness that may be revealed should be remedied by the use of drills concentrating on that particular weak point. Thus the sentence, 'He said he would do it but he hasn't done it yet', could be used to drill the Sequence of Tenses or one aspect of the Present Perfect Tense. The teacher's attention is drawn to the fact that the exercises in this book are not mechanical drills but mainly thought-provoking recall exercises, and that therefore there is little risk of boredom.

Emphasis has been placed on prepositions and phrasal verbs, always a thorny problem. Judicious use of a good dictionary will help the student to overcome some of the difficulties. It is suggested that preposition and phrasal verb exercises be done first in class, the students writing the correct answers in their notebooks. These can then be revised orally in the following lesson. Having been done orally, they can be given again as short written tests.

The paragraphs with words missing can also serve as useful passages for dictation, after the students have done the actual

1

exercises at home. I would strongly recommend this procedure, the teacher omitting the same missing words but writing them on the blackboard. The student should be notified in advance that a dictation is to be given. His revision and preparation for the test is as important as the actual dictation experience.

The earlier papers provide exercises dealing with the distinctions between various pairs of frequently confused tenses, such as the Past Simple and the Present Perfect. However, the first ten are rather easy and, at the teacher's discretion, may be done fairly quickly – or even omitted in part.

The words, 'a suitable form or tense', not 'the correct tense' are used most of the time. In such cases the student should be aware of the significance of his choice. The distinctions will always serve to clarify the complexities of the tenses. Even in the earlier exercises, where the choice is between two specified tenses, there is the occasional sentence where either is possible. These can be commented on or passed over at the discretion of the teacher.

It should be noted that (a) no explanation or notes are provided herein, this being left to the teacher's judgement, and (b) all the exercises in this workbook have been tried and tested in class.

I am indebted to my colleagues at the Pitman School for Overseas Students for their many helpful suggestions. I would also like to express my sincere thanks to Mr Maurice Moliver for his invaluable assistance in so carefully checking the manuscript.

M. POSNER
*London, March 1975*

# PAPER 1

**1** Put the verbs in parentheses into the correct tense. Use Present Simple or Present Continuous only:

EXAMPLE: He generally (*wear*) a dark suit, but today he (*wear*) a light one.

He generally wears a dark suit, but today he is wearing a light one.

a   'What you (*do*) this evening?' 'I (*stay*) at home.'
b   'Our teacher seldom (*sit*) when he (*teach*). I (*wonder*) why he (*do*) so now.' 'Perhaps he (*not feel*) well.'
c   'John (*come*) to see me this evening.' 'You (*know*) why he (*want*) to see you?' 'I (*think*) he (*need*) some advice.'
d   What you (*think*) about? You (*look*) rather worried.
e   The man who (*talk*) to John at the moment (*speak*) seven languages.
f   We (*study*) two of Shaw's plays at present.
g   When water (*freeze*), it (*change*) into ice.
h   They generally (*go*) abroad for their holidays, but this year they (*stay*) at home.
    'I (*hear*) you (*leave*) the country shortly.' 'Yes, I (*go*) to the United States. I (*expect*) to be away about three months.'
j   'What he (*do*) for a living?' 'He (*buy*) and (*sell*) antique furniture.'
k   'Why you (*keep*) looking at that photograph?' 'It (*remind*) me of my father.'
l   She (*fry*) some fish at the moment. She (*not like*) fish but her husband (*love*) it.

**2** Put in the missing prepositions:

a   What are you laughing ......... ?
b   I'm tired ......... telling him to be more careful ......... his handwriting.
c   My book is different ......... yours.
d   Please come ......... seven o'clock ......... Friday evening.
e   Walk ......... this street until you come ......... the post-office.

3

f   Which hotel are you staying ......... ?
g   Would you like to come ......... us ......... the British Museum?
h   You'll find the answer ......... the last page ......... the book.
i   I'm going out ......... a walk. I'll be back ......... 5 o'clock ......... the latest.
j   Someone threw an egg ......... the speaker. It hit him ......... the forehead.

3   Make the following sentences (a) interrogative, (b) negative; then write questions asking about the italicized words:
EXAMPLE: She is waiting *in the office*.
                Is she waiting in the office?
                She isn't waiting in the office.
                Where is she waiting?

a   They can start work *on Friday*.
b   *John* is writing *a novel*. (Two questions)
c   *The first exercise* was the most difficult.
d   He has gone to *Paris for a week*. (Two questions)
e   She has written *ten* letters today.
f   We may smoke *in the corridor*.
g   *Mary* is going to start her new job *on Friday*. (Two questions)
h   *George* is waiting *outside*. (Two questions)
i   We should leave *at nine o'clock*.
j   He is angry *because he wasn't invited*.
k   We are going to tell *the manager tomorrow*. (Two questions)
l   She ought to go *by plane*.

4   Rewrite these sentences, using *too* or *enough*:
EXAMPLES: It's very hot. I can't wear this dress.
                It's too hot (*for me*) to wear this dress.
                The amount is small. I can pay it off in one year.
                The amount is small enough (*for me*) to pay off in one year.

a   She is very young. She can't do this work.
b   It's warm. We can sit in the garden.
c   These books are expensive. I can't buy them.
d   She's very excited. She can't think of anything else.

4

e   I'm very hungry. I could eat anything.
f   The story is very complicated. I can't understand it.
g   She's quite slim. She can wear slacks.
h   I am very busy. I can't do it today.
i   The water was clean. We could swim in it.
j   The problem is difficult. I can't solve it.
k   The explanation is very simple. A child can understand it.
l   He's very tall. He can't buy ready-made clothes.

**5** Put the following sentences into Reported Speech, using the verbs given in parentheses:

EXAMPLES:   Please wait outside. (*ask*) I asked him to wait outside.
Don't tell anybody. (*tell*) He told me not to tell anybody.
Get out at once! (*order*) He ordered me to get out at once.

a   Please come back later. (*ask*)
b   Don't forget to write. (*ask*)
c   Don't make a noise. (*tell*)
d   Please speak slowly. (*ask*)
e   Hurry up! (*tell*)
f   Take the children for a walk. (*ask*)
g   Write it carefully. (*tell*)
h   Send a telegram. (*tell*)
i   Don't go out in the rain. (*tell*)
j   Put out that cigarette. (*order*)
k   Please don't make a noise. (*ask*)
l   Please don't go alone. (*ask*)

**6  Since and For**
Complete the following sentences with either *since* or *for*:

a   We haven't seen him ......... three weeks.
b   She has lived in this house ......... a long time.
c   I haven't heard from him ......... I came to England.
d   I have had this suit ......... nearly five years.
e   I haven't spoken English ......... I was a child.
f   She hasn't been here ......... last week.
g   She's been out of town ......... the last two weeks.
h   I've been waiting ......... 9 o'clock.

5

i   She's been working for the same firm ......... 1965.
j   She has been in hospital ......... five days.
k   I've known Michael ......... many years.
l   I haven't worn any other shoes ......... I bought these.

# PAPER 2

**1** Put the verbs in parentheses into the correct tense. Use Past Simple or Past Continuous only:

EXAMPLE: When I (*come*) home, the children (*do*) their homework.

When I came home, the children were doing their
homework.

a   When I (*see*) her, she (*speak*) to the waiter.
b   She (*say*) she (*leave*) the country the following day.
c   While I (*cut*) out the pictures, my wife (*paste*) them into an album.
d   When we (*arrive*) at the theatre, some other people (*sit*) in our seats.
e   I (*meet*) him while I (*go*) to the office.
f   The phone (*ring*) while I (*have*) lunch.
g   I (*do*) my homework before I (*go*) to bed. (*be careful*)
h   When our former French teacher (*speak*) to us, she (*speak*) only French.
i   When the bell (*ring*), we (*do*) a test. When it (*stop*), the teacher (*tell*) us to continue writing.
j   While I (*listen*) to the radio, my children (*do*) their homework.
k   The moment he (*hear*) the good news, he (*telephone*) me.
l   When I (*live*) in London, I often (*go*) to the theatre.

**2** Complete the phrasal verb by adding the missing particle. Choose from:

*on, out, up, back, away, off.*

a   Eat ......... your dinner or I won't let you go .........
b   Take ......... that old dress and put ......... a good one. We're going .........
c   Mary's ......... and won't be ......... before 11 o'clock.

6

d  Switch ......... all the lights before you leave.
e  John has taken me ........ twice this week.
f  When you hear your name called ........., please stand
   .........
g  Get ......... the bus here and get ......... at the third
   stop.
h  I don't feel like cooking. Let's eat ........ tonight.
i  I thought you were still ........ When did you get
   .........?
j  A button has come ......... my jacket.

3  Make the following sentences (a) interrogative, (b) negative;
then write questions asking about the italicized words:
EXAMPLE: He went *home*.
                     Did he go home?
                     He didn't go home.
                     Where did he go?

a  *John* lives *in London*. (Two questions)
b  She left *at three o'clock*.
c  She saw the film *three* times.
d  We come here *twice a week*.
e  We have lunch *in the canteen*.
f  The *French* lesson ends *at twelve o'clock*. (Two questions)
g  They meet each other *once a week*.
h  He sent it by post *because he wanted to surprise her*.
i  *Gerda* buys her clothes *in Bond Street*. (Two questions)
j  They stayed there *for an hour*.

4  Put the verbs in parentheses into the Passive Voice, using the
tenses suggested:
EXAMPLES: The house (*clean*) every day. (Present Simple)
                      The house is cleaned every day.
                      The money (*steal*) during the night. (Past Simple)
                      The money was stolen during the night.

a  The book (*leave*) on the table. (Future Simple)
b  The meal (*cook*) when I arrived. (Past Continuous)
c  The grass (*cut*) once a week. (Present Simple)
d  This suit (*make*) in England. (Past Simple)
e  The missing child (*find*). (Present Perfect)

7

f The house must (*sell*) before the end of the month. (Infinitive)
g Four different languages (*speak*) in Switzerland. (Present Simple)
h You can't go in; the house (*paint*). (Present Continuous)
i It ought (*do*) before Friday. (Infinitive)
j The book (*translate*) into many languages. (Present Perfect)

## 5 Conditional Sentences

Put the verbs in parentheses into the correct tense:

EXAMPLES: If I pass my driving test, I shall buy a car.
If I don't pass my driving test, I shan't buy a car.
I will do it if he asks me to.
Read it carefully if you want to understand it.

a If he (*not be*) here by eight o'clock, I shall go home.
b If you don't take an umbrella, you (*get*) wet.
c I (*buy*) it if the price is right.
d I will not take the room if they (*not allow*) me to use the kitchen.
e If you eat any more food, you (*not be*) able to stand up.
f If you (*not read*) the story carefully, you won't understand it.
g If you (*post*) it now, he'll get it in the morning.
h If the baby (*cry*), give him something to drink.
i I (*not go*) with you if you don't apologize.
j If you (*see*) him, tell him to telephone me.

## 6 Say and Tell

Put in the correct form of *say* or *tell*:

a He ......... me what you .......... to him last night.
b She ......... the children a story before they went to bed.
c She ......... that her child can ......... the time.
d She ......... to the children, 'You must always ......... the truth.'
e He ......... to me, '......... John what you ......... me last night.'
f He ......... me not to ......... him anything.
g She ......... to the children, 'It's wicked to ......... a lie.'
h I can't remember what he ......... to me.
i The teacher ......... that every student would have to ......... a story.

8

j   'What did you ........?' 'I never ........ a word.'
k   Don't ........ anything!
l   ........ me what he ........ the others.
m   You promised not to ........ anybody.
n   The twins are so alike, I can't ........ one from the other.
o   It is ........ that John is leaving the firm.


# PAPER 3

**1** Put the verbs in parentheses into the correct tense. Use Past Simple or Present Perfect:

EXAMPLE: Her health *has improved* since she *stopped* smoking.

a   I (*not see*) him since he (*change*) his job.
b   She (*not write*) to me since she (*leave*) England.
c   She (*not have*) any trouble since she (*have*) the operation.
d   He (*have*) five different jobs since he (*leave*) school.
e   Since he (*win*) £30,000 on the football pools, he (*not do*) a stroke of work.
f   Since I (*buy*) this car, I (*become*) very lazy.
g   I (*see*) very little of him since he (*get*) married.
h   I (*see*) him six months ago, but I (*not see*) him since.
i   I (*visit*) New York in 1966, but I (*not be*) there since.
j   Since he (*begin*) writing, his whole approach to life (*change*).
k   Since she (*start*) her new diet, she (*lose*) a lot of weight.
l   He (*not stop*) drinking since the party (*begin*).

**2** Put in the missing prepositions:

a   I can't conceal anything ........ my sister.
b   She always knows what I am thinking ........
c   It wasn't ........ good condition when I bought it.
d   Can I rely ........ you to do it?
e   I correspond ........ people from all ........ the world.
f   Try to keep your dog ........ control.
g   His pictures are excellent and are very much ........ demand.
h   ........ a man ........ his age he's ........ very good condition.

9

i   I'm grateful ......... you ......... your advice.

j   He succeeded ......... passing the examination.


**3**   Write questions asking about the italicized words:

EXAMPLE: *John* bought *a car.*

               Who bought a car? John.

               What did John buy? A car.


a   *Mary* weighs *ten stone.* (Two questions)

b   *John* has been here *since 1965.* (Two questions)

c   *The children* went to Paris *by train.* (Two questions)

d   *John* planted *six* apple-trees *in his garden.* (Three questions)

e   She couldn't get in *because she had lost her ticket.*

f   He found *the book on the floor.*

g   He intends to stay there *about a month.*

h   *Henry* found *the book in the drawer.* (Three questions)

i   The lecture will be given *in the concert hall.*

j   *Mary* is going to buy *a dress on Friday.* (Three questions)


**4**  **Omission of Relative Pronoun**

If you think the relative pronoun can be omitted, put it in parentheses:

EXAMPLE: Is this the book (*that*) you were looking for?


a   The man that we spoke to was a rather unusual person.

b   The book that you lent me was very good.

c   The man that told us that story was lying.

d   The person who owns this shop is my neighbour.

e   The picture which I bought last year is worth much more than I paid for it.

f   The house in which I was born is still standing.

g   The person that you are talking about is my nephew.

h   I met a woman whose name I can't remember.

i   The only person that understood the situation was Victor.

j   I showed him the photograph which you liked so much.


**5**  Put the following sentences into Reported Speech. The introducing verb must be in the Past Tense:

EXAMPLE: I don't know where she is going.

               He said he didn't know where she was going.

a I can't do it unless you help me.

b I met him in Paris last month.

c I have finished the book at last.

d I'm sorry I won't be able to go.

e This isn't what I ordered.

f I'll be here tomorrow.

g John is arriving tonight.

h I must go and see him before he leaves.

i If you do that again, I shall be very angry.

j I'd like to speak to you when the lesson is over.


**6** Complete the following sentences by putting in a suitable gerund in the blank space:

EXAMPLE: I enjoy ........ on a cold day.

               I enjoy *walking* on a cold day.

a Thank you for ........ me how to get there.

b She began ........ the story last week and hasn't stopped ........ about it.

c I hate ........ in a queue.

d Would you mind ........ outside?

e I prefer ........ to ........ by bus.

f I wanted to give him a lift but he insisted on ........ on foot.

g I remember ........ you in Rome two years ago.

h He denied ........ the money.

i If you keep on ........ a noise, I shall call the police.

j My doctor told me to avoid ........ starchy foods. I should have had a good dinner before ........ to see him.


# PAPER 4

**1** Put the verbs in parentheses into the correct tense. Use Present Perfect (Simple or Continuous) only:

EXAMPLE: I have been waiting for two hours but nobody has arrived yet.

a I (*read*) for the last two hours, but I (*not finish*) half the story yet.

b I (*write*) ever since I got up and I only (*write*) three letters.
c I (*study*) French for the last three years.
d He (*be promoted*) three times since he (*work*) here.
e The picture (*hang*) in the same place ever since I bought it.
f He (*write*) a book for the last six months but (*make*) very little progress so far.
g I (*visit*) many countries in the last five years.
h I (*shop*) all the morning, but I (*not buy*) anything yet.
i Someone (*take*) my book. I (*look*) for it for the last ten minutes but I can't see it anywhere.
j The telephone (*ring*) four times since I (*sit*) here.

2 Complete the phrasal verbs by putting in the missing particle. Choose from:

*back, up, off, away, out, in, with.*

a 'Put ......... your tongue,' said the doctor.
b Luckily the bomb didn't go .........
c He stayed ......... all night listening to the election results.
d The police had difficulty in keeping ......... the crowds.
e I've used ......... all my paint. Can I have some of yours?
f Some parents don't know how to bring ......... children.
g Please don't give ......... my secret.
h What time does the train get .........?
i The shoes are nice, but they won't go ......... my dress.
j Don't touch it! Wait until it cools .........
k He worked quickly so that he would be able to get ......... early.
l The plane took ......... five minutes late.

3 Join the two sentences by making the second a relative clause. Omit the pronoun wherever possible.
EXAMPLES: The man is a detective. He is standing in the corner.
          The man who is standing in the corner is a detective.
          This is the man. We spoke to him last week.
          This is the man we spoke to last week.

a I showed him the letter. I received it this morning.
b The house is beautiful. My uncle lives in it.
c That is the boy. He broke your window.
d I met the man. You sold your car to him.

e  I met the man. His daughter works in our office.
f  I have seen the film. You are talking about it.
g  The people are very kind. I am staying with them.
h  He received the letter. He was waiting for it.
i  I know the boy. He married your sister.

## 4  Conditional Sentences (unreal or improbable)

Put the verbs in parentheses into the correct tense:

EXAMPLES:  If I had time, I (*study*) French.
 If I had time, I would study French.

a  If I could make my own clothes, I (*save*) a lot of money.
b  If I were younger, I (*study*) languages.
c  If the men (*get*) higher salaries, they would work harder.
d  If my watch (*stop*), I would try to repair it.
e  Your suit would look better if you (*wear*) another tie.
f  I would paint the house myself if I (*be*) able to do it.
g  If he (*not eat*) so much, he would be healthier.
h  If the room (*not be*) so small, we could put more furniture in it.
i  I would eat more fish if it (*not be*) so dear.
j  If I could use a typewriter, I (*save*) a lot of time.

## 5  *There is, It is*

Put in the correct form of *it is* or *there is*:

EXAMPLES:  ......... very cold yesterday.
 It was very cold yesterday.
 ......... somebody in the room now.
 There is somebody in the room now.

a  ......... an interesting film at the cinema this week.
b  ......... nobody there when I called.
c  ......... obvious why he did it.
d  ......... still many people who are superstitious.
e  ......... very few people there when I arrived.
f  The radio says ......... very warm tomorrow.
g  Put on your coat; ......... time to go.
h  ......... important to know the rules of grammar?
i  ......... a long way from your house to the station?
j  ......... a pity you weren't there.
k  ......... some ice-cream in the refrigerator.
l  ......... rather strange that he wasn't invited.

**6** Write sentences to show that the following words can be used as nouns or verbs:

| | | | |
|---|---|---|---|
| drink | water | hand | brush |
| dress | wish | comb | swim |

EXAMPLE: I'm going for a *swim*. (noun)
Can you *swim*? (verb)

# PAPER 5

**1** Put the verbs in parentheses into a correct tense. Use Past Simple or Past Perfect only:

EXAMPLE: When I (*arrive*), the party already (*begin*).
When I arrived, the party had already begun.

a   I (*wait*) until everybody (*leave*).
b   The teacher (*be*) very angry when he (*see*) what the boys (*do*).
c   I (*not be*) there five minutes when all the lights (*go*) out.
d   When I (*show*) him what I (*write*), he (*say*) it (*be*) very good.
e   By the time we (*get*) there, most of the guests (*arrive*).
f   He (*thank*) me for what I (*do*) and (*say*) I (*be*) a great help to him.
g   As soon as I (*do*) it, I (*realize*) that I (*make*) a mistake.
h   He (*not tell*) anybody what he (*do*).
i   I'm sorry. I (*think*) I (*tell*) you.
j   The students (*be*) in the classroom more than ten minutes when the teacher finally (*arrive*).
k   Although he (*study*) English before he (*go*) to England, he never (*hear*) the language spoken so quickly. At first he (*not understand*) anything, but when he (*be*) there about six months, he (*be*) able to carry on a conversation.

**2** Put in the missing prepositions:

a   This style of clothing is very popular ......... teenagers.
b   A dog is faithful ......... its master.
c   He's very critical ......... my work.
d   You must be patient ......... him.
e   She's jealous ......... her friend's success.
f   Fresh air is good ......... you.

14

g  Your face is familiar ......... me.
h  I am very much obliged ......... you ......... your help.
i  If you compare my work ......... his, you will see the difference.
j  You must concentrate ......... what you are doing.

**3**  Put the following sentences into Reported Speech:
EXAMPLE:  Is he coming?
          He asked if/whether he was coming.

a  Will John be there?
b  Have you finished your work?
c  Can you help me to find my cat?
d  Is it raining?
e  Are you leaving tomorrow?
f  Were you here last week?
g  Must I do it straight away?
h  May I go with them?
i  Need I tell him?
j  Will you be here tomorrow?
k  Would you like to come with us?
l  Did you see John take my book?

**4**  Put in the missing words. Choose from the following:

| while | besides | because of | however |
| although | since | unless | therefore |
| except | during | so that | in spite of |

a  He couldn't take part in the race ......... his bad leg.
b  ......... the weather is bad, we'd better phone for a taxi.
c  I thought he was an intelligent person; ........., it seems I was mistaken.
d  Not many people came to the concert ......... the great publicity.
e  She won't go ......... you call for her.
f  ......... the team played well, they were beaten quite easily.
g  All the students came to the party ......... Gerda.
h  I have two other umbrellas ......... this one.
i  There were several interruptions ......... the lecture.
j  I lent him the money ......... he might go to the concert.

15

k He is a kind and helpful person; ......... he is liked by everybody.

l He fell asleep ......... he was watching television.

**5** Change the following sentences from plural to singular:

a These children speak better than those children.

b Our sons go to school by themselves.

c Babies cannot dress themselves.

d When they go to London, they usually go by train.

e They are very good children. We never have any trouble with them.

f Our teachers do not give us homework every day.

g Good workers are proud of their work.

h Can dogs wash themselves?

i The men in the other room work very hard.

j Do they know what the children were doing all day?

k They have been very good to us.

l The books on those shelves are textbooks.

**6** Complete the sentences by adding one of the following words: *much, many, little, few, less,* or *fewer.*

a How *many* chairs will you need?

b I work hard all day. I have *little* time for hobbies.

c How *much* flour will I need for the cake?

d He's a wonderful person. There are *many* people who would do the things he does.

e There are ......... people here today than there were last week.

f I have *less* money than you.

g If you ate ......... bread, you wouldn't put on so *much* weight.

h 'Every ......... helps,' said the person who was collecting money for charity.

i Hurry up! We have very *little* time.

j We have done ......... work today than we did yesterday.

k I have *fewer* mistakes than you have.

l Although he is a very rich man, he spends *little* money on clothes.

16

# PAPER 6

**1** Put the verbs in parentheses into the correct tense. Use Present Simple or Future Simple only:

EXAMPLE: I shall wait until he goes.

a   I (*clean*) the house after the children (*go*) to school.
b   When you (*return*), you (*see*) the difference.
c   I (*send*) you a telegram as soon as I (*hear*) the good news.
d   Please wait until I (*find*) out where he is.
e   I must do the shopping before my husband (*come*) home.
f   When I (*grow*) up, I (*want*) to be a doctor.
g   I (*pay*) you when I (*get*) my salary.
h   I (*not let*) the house until I (*find*) a suitable tenant.
i   I am sure he (*find*) a job when he (*come*) to London.
j   By the time we (*arrive*), the place (*be*) empty.
k   I never (*forget*) you as long as I (*live*).
l   I (*wash*) the dishes while you (*clean*) up the room.

**2** Complete the following sentences by putting in the missing particle. Choose from:

*out, about, for, down, on, off, up.*

a   His name will certainly go ......... in history.
b   Please go ......... with your work.
c   How long will they be able to hold ......... without further supplies reaching them?
d   Hold .........! I'm going with you.
e   Fortunately, the rain held ......... until we returned.
f   We've been invited ......... to dinner.
g   Keep your coat ......... We're leaving in a few minutes.
h   They quarrelled a few days ago but they've made it ......... now.
i   Stop ordering me .........! I don't work for you.
j   With his accent he could easily pass ......... an American.

**3** Complete the sentences by putting in one of the following words:

*some, any, one, ones.*

a   Are there ......... tickets left? I need .........

17

b   I asked the secretary if there were ..*some*.. tickets but she had only the expensive ..*ones*.. left.

c   'Have you ..*any*.. oranges?' 'Yes, I bought ..*some*.. in the market.'

d   If you have ..*some*.. juicy ..*ones*.., I'd like ..*some*..

e   Please put ..*some*.. apples on the table. There are hardly ..*any*.. left.

f   I doubt whether ..*any*.. of the shops are open, but if you really want ..*some*.. milk, I can easily borrow ..*some*.. from the neighbour.

g   'She has ..*some*.. beautiful dresses. Did you see the ..*one*.. she wore at the party?' 'Which party? She wears a different ..*one*.. at every party.'

h   Would you like ........ more coffee? I'm sure you would.

i   If there are ..*any*.. cucumbers in the shop, please buy ..*some*..

j   I need a good dictionary. Can you recommend ..*one*..?

k   'I bought ..*some*.. second-hand books.' 'Were there ..*any*.. interesting ........ among them?' 'Yes, I found ........ good ........'

l   There's hardly ..*any*.. sugar in the house. You'd better go out and buy ........

4   Put the adverb in parentheses into the correct place in the sentence:

a   I have to tell him more than once. (never)
b   We are busy at this time of the year. (usually)
c   I have seen such a beautiful sunset. (seldom)
d   We have lunch together. (often)
e   You ought to have told him. (never)
f   What's wrong with the service? We used to wait so long. (never)
g   I am tired at the end of the day. (quite, usually)
h   Do you play cards? (ever)
i   He's a very diligent pupil. He comes late. (rarely)
j   Is he so bad-tempered? (always)

5   Conditional Sentences.
Put the verbs in brackets into the correct tense:

18

EXAMPLES: If I had known, I would have gone.
I would have helped you if you had asked me to.

a    If I (*not be*) so tired, I would have gone with you.
b    If he had ordered me, I (*have*) to go.
c    If you had been more careful, you not (*break*) it.
d    If he (*not go*), she would have been very upset.
e    I would have told him if I (*see*) him.
f    I (*have*) lunch if I hadn't been in such a hurry.
g    I (*catch*) the train if I had left five minutes earlier.
h    If you (*warn*) me earlier, I (*not invite*) him. Now it's too late.
i    If the weather (*be*) better, we would have enjoyed the trip more.
j    'If I hadn't already seen the film, I (*go*) with them.

**6**  Add question-tags to the following:
EXAMPLES: He speaks French, doesn't he?
They won't be there, will they?

a    They have been here before, . . . . . . . . . ?
b    He wouldn't do a thing like that, . . . . . . . . . ?
c    He speaks Italian, . . . . . . . . . ?
d    You didn't really tell him, . . . . . . . . . ?
e    They weren't angry, . . . . . . . . . ?
f    They don't like cats, . . . . . . . . . ?
g    She's very charming, . . . . . . . . . ?
h    He couldn't solve the problem, . . . . . . . . . ?
i    He wasn't there, . . . . . . . . . ?
j    You've had lunch, . . . . . . . . . ?

# PAPER 7

**1**  Put the verbs in brackets into the correct tense. Use Future Perfect or Present Perfect only.
EXAMPLES: By twelve o'clock everybody *will have left*.
When everybody *has left*, I'll clean the house.

a    By five o'clock the children (*return*) from their walk.
b    When they (*wash*) themselves, I will give them something to eat.

19

c   I hope we (*sell*) all the tickets before the end of the week.
d   By the time they return, I (*finish*) all my housework.
e   When I (*write*) the letter, I'll show it to you.
f   By the end of this term, we (*read*) two novels and six short stories.
g   As soon as I (*save*) enough money, I'll get a new car.
h   When we (*finish*) reading this story, I'll give you a test.
i   By the time I leave England, I (*see*) more than fifteen different plays.
j   When I (*be*) in England as long as you have, shall I be able to speak English as well as you do?
k   You are not to go to work until you completely (*recover*).
l   When you (*be*) with the firm six months, your salary will be increased.

**2**   Put in the missing prepositions:

a   If you apply ......... a transfer, you might get one.
b   He is very much attached ......... his family.
c   They are no longer ......... war ......... their neighbours.
d   He was found unfit ......... military service.
e   She suffers ......... very bad headaches.
f   I've had this bicycle for a long time. I wouldn't like to part ......... it.
g   He's incapable ......... doing such a thing.
h   Which party are you voting ......... in the election?
i   He died ......... pneumonia.
j   This blanket is made ......... wool.

**3**   Complete the following sentences by giving the correct form of the words in parentheses:
EXAMPLE: (*beauty*) It's a ......... day.
                    It's a beautiful day.

a   (*edit*) The new ......... will be published shortly.
b   (*economy*) We must ......... on fuel.
c   (*economy*) We must be more .........
d   (*economy*) The ......... situation is very bad.
e   (*exist*) It's one of the oldest manuscripts in .........
f   (*exclude*) The price quoted is ......... of tax.
g   (*envy*) She is ......... of her neighbour's success.

h  (*length*) You should ......... your trousers.
i  (*vary*) Her cooking is good but it lacks .........
j  (*succeed*) He is a ......... writer.

**4**  Rewrite the following sentences, using *unless* instead of *if not*.

EXAMPLES:  I won't go if he doesn't go.
          I won't go unless he goes.

a  He won't pass the examination if he doesn't work harder.
b  I will not go if you don't take the car.
c  I wouldn't say so if I were not certain.
d  You won't like it if you don't read it aloud.
e  She won't go if you don't invite her sister as well.
f  I shan't go if the weather doesn't improve.
g  He would never go anywhere if I didn't take him.
h  If we don't leave immediately, we shall be late.
i  I don't like soup if it is not hot.
j  Don't go if you don't really want to.

**5**  Answer each question with a complete answer:

EXAMPLE:  What will you do if the weather is fine tomorrow?
          If the weather is fine tomorrow, I shall go to the park.

a  What would you do if the teacher didn't give you any homework?
b  What would you do if you lost your pen?
c  What would you have done if the teacher had not come to school today?
d  What will you do if it rains tomorrow?
e  What might happen if you drove very fast?
f  What will the teacher say if you don't do your homework?
g  What would you have done if you had seen me yesterday?
h  What will you do if I ask you to tell a story?
i  What would you do if you won £50,000?
j  What will you say if I ask you to lend me some money?

**6**  The following words have been omitted from the paragraph. Put them back in the correct places:

| | | | | |
|---|---|---|---|---|
| sums | especially | reckless | fast | realize |
| increase | lawful | tempted | prefer | citizens |

Some people think that the police should always be armed,
.......... in these days when bandits use .......... cars and
attack helpless .......... who are carrying large .......... of
money. But the police .......... the present system. They know
that .......... criminals might be .......... to fire at them if
they themselves carried arms, and they .......... that this would
.......... the danger to ordinary men and women who are
walking about the streets on their .......... business.

# PAPER 8

**1**  Put the verbs in parentheses into the correct tense. Use Present
Perfect or Past Simple only. Pay attention to word order:

a  When I first (*meet*) him, he (*speak*) very little English; however, in the last few months he (*make*) considerable progress.

b  I (*know*) him since he (*be*) a child.

c  How long ago he (*leave*)?

d  He just (*go*) out. He (*say*) he (*have*) an appointment.

e  'Where you (*buy*) that book?' 'I (*not buy*) it; I (*borrow*) it
from a friend.'

f  Who (*write*) 'Robinson Crusoe'?

g  Business never (*be*) so good as it is today.

h  It (*not stop*) raining since I (*come*) here. Perhaps I am exag-
gerating, but it (*rain*) every day this week.

i  I wonder why she (*marry*) him.

j  I often (*see*) him but I never (*speak*) to him.

k  'How you (*enjoy*) the film?' 'It's one of the best films I ever
(*see*).'

l  I (*write*) to him some time ago, but I (*not receive*) a reply yet.

**2**  Complete the phrasal verbs by putting in the missing particles.
Choose from:
*down, up, after, off, out, to.*

a  Please look .......... the baby while I am ..........

b  Our car broke ..........; we had to walk most of the way.

c  I never studied English. I picked it .......... while I was
working in England.

d  Prices have gone ............ quite a lot recently.

e  I'm relying on you. Don't let me .........

f  Has it left ......... raining yet?

g  He started ......... as an office boy and ended ......... as managing director.

h  If you don't write it ........., you'll forget it.

i  She wrote ......... the cheque and asked him to sign it.

j  She needed advice but had nobody to turn .........

## 3  Clauses of Reason

Join the following pairs of sentences using the words supplied in parentheses:

EXAMPLES:  It was raining. I took an umbrella. (*since*)
           Since it was raining, I took an umbrella.
           There were no more buses. We took a taxi. (*because*)
           We took a taxi because there were no more buses.

a  He didn't pass the examination. His mother was upset. (*because*)

b  We have a holiday tomorrow. We don't have to get up early. (*since*)

c  He has lost a lot of blood. He is very weak. (*seeing that*)

d  The students had gone to bed very late. They were very tired the following morning. (*as*)

e  The fog was very thick. We couldn't drive any farther. (*because*)

f  I don't expect he will get the job. His English is so poor. (*seeing that*)

g  His composition was very bad. I told him to write it again. (*since*)

h  There's not much food in the house. We'll go out for dinner. (*as*)

i  His temperature has gone down. He can get up tomorrow. (*since*)

j  He went home early. He had to go to the dentist. (*because*)

## 4  Adverb Order

Put the adverbs in parentheses in the correct place in the sentence:

EXAMPLE:  I go (*in summer, usually, to Paris*).
          I usually go to Paris in summer.

a   We meet (*on Sunday afternoon, in the park, always*).
b   I saw John (*in the office, about an hour ago*).
c   I have a cup of tea (*in bed, always, before I get up*).
d   We must invite them (*next week, to our house*).
e   I get up early (*on Sunday, seldom*).
f   He plays (*well, in an important game, always*).
g   We eat (*usually, when we go to the theatre, out*).
h   He spoke (*very well, at the debate, last night*).
i   He arrived (*at the meeting, at eight o'clock*).
j   We are meeting (*tomorrow, at John's house, at nine o'clock*).

5   Write questions to which the following could be answers:

a   I'm afraid he's not at home.
b   I think so.
c   I hope not.
d   The blue one, please.
e   Leave it on the table.
f   Yes, I have to.
g   I've no idea.
h   I did.
i   In the refrigerator, please.
j   I thought it was rather dull.

6   Put the following sentences into Reported Speech:
EXAMPLE:   Where are you going?
            He asked me where I was going.

a   What does John want?
b   How long has Gerda been in England?
c   Why is the baby crying?
d   How much did you pay for your refrigerator?
e   When will you be here again?
f   Why didn't you do your homework?
g   What time must we be there?
h   How often do you go to the theatre?
i   Where does Mary work?
j   Why aren't you going to the concert?
k   How long have you been waiting here?
l   How soon can you finish the work?

24

# PAPER 9

**1** Put the verbs in parentheses into a correct tense:

a She said she (*not finish*) the book yet.

b How long you (*sit*) here? I (*not see*) you come in.

c He (*leave*) his job last month and (*be*) out of work ever since.

d 'When are you getting married?' 'I (*get*) married as soon as I (*find*) a house.'

e 'Can I speak to John?' 'I am afraid he (*have*) a bath at the moment.'

f When I (*see*) him, he (*clean*) his car. He (*do*) this every Sunday.

g When I (*finish*) the book, I'll lend it to you.

h If he had asked me, I (*tell*) him.

i It (*rain*) ever since I (*get*) up this morning. If it (*not stop*) soon, I (*have*) to change my programme.

j I just (*buy*) a new dress. Would you like to see it?

k When we (*arrive*) at the theatre, the play already (*begin*). We (*not be allowed*) to take our seats until the first act (*end*).

l Please (*wait*) until I (*come*) back.

**2** Put in the missing prepositions:

a Who were you talking . . . . . . . ., just now?

b What were you talking . . . . . . . .?

c I have no respect . . . . . . . . such people.

d The house . . . . . . . . the corner is . . . . . . . . sale.

e Are you really serious . . . . . . . . going to Australia?

f He fell . . . . . . . . love . . . . . . . . the new secretary.

g It was love . . . . . . . . first sight.

h Are you familiar . . . . . . . . this part . . . . . . . . town?

i That style . . . . . . . . dress is no longer . . . . . . . . fashion.

j She's . . . . . . . . a very bad mood.

**3** Put the following conversations into Reported Speech.

EXAMPLES: 'Are you going?' 'Yes.'

He asked me whether I was going and I said I was.

'Can you swim?' 'No, I can't.'

He asked me if I could swim and I told him I couldn't.

25

a 'Have you seen the film?' 'No.'
b 'Shall I close the window?' 'Yes, please.'
c 'Were you at the party?' 'No, I wasn't.'
d 'Would you do it if she asked you?' 'Yes, I would.'
e 'Is there any beer in the refrigerator?' 'Yes.'
f 'Will George be there?' 'No.'
g 'Did you go out last night?' 'Yes.'
h 'May I use your phone?' 'Yes.'
i 'Do you smoke?' 'No.'
j 'Must you go?' 'Yes.'

**4** Put the following sentences into the Passive Voice. Don't use 'by' in any of the sentences:
EXAMPLE: They took the children to the park.
     The children were taken to the park.

a Nobody can do such a thing.
b They are building a new garage here.
c They told us to be here at nine o'clock.
d I shall leave the key under the mat.
e We haven't seen George for a long time.
f We must settle the matter before we leave.
g I have ironed your trousers.
h When did they last paint the house?
i They must sell the house before the end of the month.
j They thought somebody was following them.

**5 Adjectives and Adverbs**
Write the following sentences choosing the correct form of the words in parentheses – adjective or adverb:
EXAMPLES: She sang the song (*beautiful*).
     She sang the song beautifully.
     He has always been a very (*careful*) worker.
     He has always been a very careful worker.

a Some of the passengers were very (*bad*) injured.
b Please speak (*slow*). I can't understand you when you speak (*quick*).
c He works very (*hard*).
d He looks rather (*strange*) to me.
e He looked at me (*strange*).

f He speaks English very (*good*).

g I am not (*complete*) satisfied.

h He feels (*unhappy*) about the situation.

i Why do you look so (*unhappy*)?

j This coffee tastes very (*good*).

k He is (*happy*) married.

l He seemed (*angry*) although he spoke (*calm*).

m He will behave (*different*) when he understands the (*true*) situation.

n Does he (*usual*) speak so (*good*)?

o Please don't drive so (*fast*). Be (*careful*).

6 The following words have been omitted from the paragraph. Put them back into the correct places:

harness   ground   wants   simple
wove   provide   produced   spun   hides

The villagers did not need any shops, for their ........ were few and ........ They themselves could ........ most of the things they needed. Their sheep ........ the wool that the women ........ into yarn and ........ into cloth. The ........ of their cattle gave them leather for shoes and ........ Wheat and rye were ........ into flour for bread-making.

# PAPER 10

1 Put the verbs in parentheses into the correct tense. Pay attention to word order:

a When I (*arrive*) at the airport half an hour late, I (*find*) that the plane already (*leave*).

b I (*be told*) that I (*have*) to wait an hour for the next one.

c While I (*wait*) in the airport lounge I (*see*) a friend of mine.

d It turned out that he, too, (*go*) to Amsterdam.

e He said he (*go*) on business and (*be*) there about a week.

f I (*be*) glad that I (*miss*) the plane; for if I (*catch*) it, I (*not see*) my friend.

27

g  By a strange coincidence we (*find*) that we (*reserve*) rooms in the same hotel.

h  I (*like*) Amsterdam very much and (*be*) there many times.

i  If I had to live in another city for a year, I (*think*) I (*choose*) Amsterdam.

j  I always (*find*) the people there kind and helpful.


**2**  Complete phrasal verbs by adding the missing particle. Choose from:

*through, up, down, out, back, away, into, off.*

a  Some of the words had been crossed ..........

b  Don't run ..........; I want to talk to you.

c  The car won't start because the battery has run ..........

d  When I look .......... I can see the mistakes I made in my youth.

e  I lost control of the car and ran .......... a wall.

f  Turn .......... the radio. I hate that music.

g  Would you mind turning .......... the radio. It's rather loud.

h  I got .......... quite a lot of work today.

i  The examination was rather difficult, but I think I got ..........

j  When I grow .........., I want to be a pilot.


**3**  Put in the missing words. Choose from:

*since, for, ago, while, during, before.*

a  Did anyone call .......... my absence?

b  Three people called .......... you were out.

c  I saw Frank two weeks .......... but I haven't seen him ..........

d  I was in Rome .......... two weeks.

e  He began the course three weeks .........., but he had studied English ..........

f  I worked .......... the summer holidays.

g  I'm going out .......... a short time. Please look after the baby .......... I am out.

h  I have learned a great deal .......... I came to England.

i  I had learned a great deal .......... I came to England.

j  Three years .......... I was in Istanbul .......... a month.

28

**4**   Complete the following sentences by giving the correct form of the words in parentheses:

a   (*blood*) My nose is .........

b   (*delight*) What a ......... surprise!

c   (*sign*) The bank has a copy of your .........

d   (*prove, guilty*) Have you got ......... of his .........?

e   (*grateful*) How can I show my .........?

f   (*succeed*) ......... does not come easily. It must be worked for.

g   (*disturb*) There was a ......... at the back of the hall.

h   (*excel*) He spoke ......... in the debate.

i   (*pray*) Have you said your .........?

j   (*recover*) The patient made a speedy .........

**5**   Complete the following sentences, using *is* or *are*:

a   None of the students ......... standing.

b   Neither of them ......... going.

c   My trousers ......... too long.

d   The police ......... looking for you.

e   The scissors ......... not very sharp.

f   Either George or Bill ......... going to be there.

g   The news ......... not very good today.

h   The herd of horses ......... worth a lot of money.

i   Twenty pounds ......... not a lot of money today.

j   His advice ......... always worth listening to.

k   ......... either of these pens yours?

l   Mathematics ......... my favourite subject.

m   Both George and Mary ......... fond of music.

n   All the students ......... going to take the test.

**6**   Write sentences to show that the following words may be used both as verbs and nouns:

*measure, cut, work, play, ride tie.*

29

# PAPER 11

**1** Put the verbs in parentheses into a correct tense.

a I (*not see*) him for over two years.
b He (*work*) for the same firm since 1960.
c I (*see*) him now. He (*talk*) to John.
d I generally (*get*) up early, but I (*not do*) so yesterday.
e What time he usually (*arrive*)?
f I (*do*) this crossword puzzle for the last hour, but I (*not* finish) half of it yet.
g He generally (*speak*) to me in English, but at home he (*speak*) French.
h He (*wait*) for her since 6 o'clock, but she (not come) yet.
i When I (*come*) home last night, she (*cook*) dinner. In fact, she (*work*) in the kitchen for more than an hour when I (*arrive*).
j I (*meet*) him while I (*come*) here this morning.

**2** Put in the missing prepositions:

a I'm proud ........ my work.
b A good worker should take pride ........ his work.
c He was accused ........ stealing a watch.
d He was found guilty ........ the crime.
e He insisted ........ going alone.
f He says he is innocent ........ the crime.
g He charged me two pounds ........ repairing my radio.
h He is always ........ debt.
i He described the scene ........ detail.
j I cannot agree ........ his conditions.

**3** Write questions to which the following sentences could be answers, asking about the italicized words:
EXAMPLE: He bought *three* pairs.
          How many pairs of shoes did he buy?

a The book was left *on the table*.
b He paid for it *by cheque*.
c You must speak to him *in English*.
d *John* danced with *Mary* the whole evening. (Two questions)
e *Henry* is going to finish it *tomorrow*. (Two questions)

30

f    *The green one* costs *fifty pounds* (Two questions)
g    He hasn't seen his daughter for *six months.*
h    Pauline speaks *French* at *home.* (Two questions)
i    He has been working here *since 1963.*
j    *John* found *the book under the table.* (Three questions)

**4**    Put in the missing relative pronoun. If it can be omitted, put it in parentheses.
EXAMPLE: He is the only person (*that*) I can really trust.

a    The picture ......... was stolen is a very valuable one.
b    The man ......... stole it knew what he was looking for.
c    The man ......... picture was stolen is very upset.
d    The person ......... house I bought has gone abroad.
e    That's the man ......... I sold my car to.
f    The book ......... was lying on the table has disappeared.
g    The poems ......... he wrote are going to be published.
h    Is there a shop near here ......... sells cigarettes?
i    Is that the man ......... you wanted to speak to?
j    It's very difficult to find people ......... are reliable.

**5**    Put the following sentences into the Passive Voice:
EXAMPLE:    I'll clean the house after they remove the furniture.
           The house will be cleaned after the furniture is removed.

a    They were cleaning the room when I arrived.
b    We should abolish such laws.
c    They have found the missing child.
d    How much money did he steal?
e    We must do it before we paint the house. (Two passives)
f    When did he deliver the goods?
g    They publish many new books every year.
h    Why didn't they tell me earlier?
i    You must tell him before he leaves.
j    She should do it as soon as possible.

**6**    Write sentences to show clearly the difference between the two words in each of the following pairs:

| accept | adopt | interested | it's | whose |
| except | adapt | interesting | its | who's |

31

# PAPER 12

**1** Put the verbs in parentheses into a suitable form. Pay attention to word order:

When I (*come*) home, I (*find*) that the family already (*finish*) dinner. I (*sit*) down (*eat*) mine, which (*be*) still on the table. I only just (*begin*) when the door-bell (*ring*). It (*be*) a friend of mine. I (*tell*) him (*wait*) until I (*finish*) (*eat*). My mother (*ask*) him whether he (*like*) a cup of coffee. He (*say*) he rather (*read*) until I (*be*) ready.

**2** Change the following questions to an indirect form. Begin each sentence with the words given in parentheses:

EXAMPLES: Where did he go? (*I don't know* .........)
I don't know where he went.
Where does he live? (*Do you know* .........)
Do you know where he lives?

a Where did he learn to speak English so well? (*I wonder* .........)
b How long has he been here? (*Have you any idea* ʰᵒʷ.....)
c What time must we be there? (*Please ask him* .........)
d Will he be here next week? (*I'd like to know* .........)
e When does he usually take his holiday? (*Do you know* .........)
f Can he do it alone? (*I must know* .........)
g Why did he do it? (*Nobody seems to know* .........)
h Does he know her? (*Ask him* .........)
i Have we done this exercise before? (*I'm not sure* .........)
j Who took my book? (*He wants to know* .........)

**3** Complete the phrasal verbs by putting in the missing particle. Choose from:

*aside, back, off, up, on, forward, down, out.*

a The rebellion was easily put .........
b The meeting was put ......... until the following week.
c Please put ......... all the lights before you leave.
d He has put ......... a lot of weight recently.
e The clock is fast; please put it ......... ten minutes.

32

f  The clock is slow; please put it ......... ten minutes.
g  I put ......... five pounds every month so as to have enough money for my annual holiday.
h  If you know the answer, please put ......... your hand.
i  My uncle is prepared to put ......... the necessary capital.
j  Can you put me ......... for the night?

4  Put the verbs in parentheses into the correct tense:

a  If she invites him, he (go).
b  If the weather (be) bad, they won't go out.
c  I would go more often if I (have) the time.
d  I (not go) if you don't go with me.
e  If I had known earlier, I (go).
f  I may go if the weather (be) fine.
g  I wouldn't say so unless I (be) certain.
h  I must work hard if I (want) to do well in the examination.
i  I would have finished it if I (have) a little more time.
j  Take a taxi if you (want) to get there on time.

5  Fill in the blank spaces with either *mustn't* or *needn't*:

a  She ......... go to bed early; tomorrow is a holiday.
b  A rich man ......... work hard.
c  You ......... take an umbrella; I'm sure it won't rain.
d  You ......... cross the road when the lights are red.
e  You ......... tell anybody what I've just told you. It's a secret.
f  You ......... go to the bank. I can lend you the money.
g  You ......... finish it if you aren't hungry.
h  You ......... smoke in here. It's forbidden.
i  You ......... drive a car if you've been drinking.
j  You ......... warm it. I like cold coffee.

6  The following words have been omitted from the paragraph. Put them back in the correct places:

| | | |
|---|---|---|
| inventions | strides | way |
| mankind | quite | jet |
| power | during | drugs |

......... the past fifty years ......... has made many vast
......... Think of some of the great discoveries and .........

that have changed our ........ of life: radio and television, aircraft and ........ engines, ........ like insulin and penicillin that save thousands of lives, talking pictures, radar and atomic ........ You could make ........ a long list.

# PAPER 13

**1** Put the verbs in parentheses into a correct form:

One day while I (*sit*) in a café, a man (*come*) over to my table and (*ask*) me if he (*may*) (*sit*) down for a few minutes. After (*speak*) for some time, we (*find*) that we once (*meet*) in Europe. He said, 'I (*arrive*) here two weeks ago and I yet (*not make*) up my mind whether or not (*stay*) here.' 'If I (*be*) you,' I said, 'I (*learn*) the language as quickly as I (*can*) and then (*make*) a tour of the country. It (*be*) easier then (*make*) up your mind.'

**2** Put in the missing prepositions:

a   What is your reason ........ doing such a thing?
b   I am preparing ........ an examination.
c   He is leaving ........ Paris tomorrow.
d   Don't worry ........ it. I'll see ........ everything.
e   He was not accepted ........ the university.
f   I'll deal ........ the matter later.
g   He deals ........ antique furniture.
h   The public gave generously ........ response ........ the appeal.
i   He was charged ........ having stolen a watch.
j   He was complimented ........ his appearance.

**3** Put the following sentences into Reported Speech:
EXAMPLE:   How long have you known him?
                He asked me how long I had known him.

a   What did you do last night?
b   Shall I close the window? It's rather draughty.
c   Wait outside. I'll tell you when to come in.
d   Do you usually do your homework in the evening?

34

e   May I smoke here? Somebody said it's forbidden.
f   How long have you been working here?
g   Have you had lunch yet? I'm going out for mine.
h   Don't go unless he apologizes. He needs a lesson.
i   Please leave it on the table. I may need it later.
j   It's rather cold outside. Put on your coat.

4   Complete the following sentences by using the correct form of
the words in parentheses:
EXAMPLE: (*die*) His ......... came as a great shock to all of us.
            His death came as a great shock to all of us.

a   (*high*) What is the ......... of this building?
b   (*suspect*) Why are you looking at me so .........?
c   (*ridicule*) Your attitude is .........
d   (*proud*) He ......... himself on his appearance.
e   (*generous*) I was amazed at his .........
f   (*collect*) Many nations believe in ......... security.
g   (*responsible*) He is an excellent worker but he dislikes
    .........
h   (*long, wide*) What is the ......... and ......... of this
    room?
i   (*suit*) I don't think this is a ......... place for a camp.
j   (*speak*) Churchill made many great .........

5   Put in the collective noun. Choose from the following:

| pack | herd | flight | bouquet |
|---|---|---|---|
| swarm | flock | staff | gang |
| bunch | team | range | audience |

*a*   a ......... of sheep.        b   a ......... of stairs.
c     a ......... of thieves.      d   a ......... of flies.
e     a ......... of grapes.       f   a ......... of mountains.
g     a ......... of flowers.      h   a ......... of cows.
i     a ......... of teachers.     j   a ......... of footballers.
k     a ......... of cards.        l   an ......... at a lecture.

6 · Write sentences to show the difference between the two words
in each of the following pairs:

| for | beside | through | alike | rob |
|---|---|---|---|---|
| during | besides | thorough | likely | steal |

# PAPER 14

**1** Put the verbs in brackets into a correct form:

While I (*stand*) in the bank, I (*meet*) my old friend Sally, whom I (*not see*) for some time. I (*ask*) her how she (*be*) and where she (*go*) after she (*complete*) her business at the bank. She (*say*) she (*have*) nothing special (*do*) as she (*not work*) then. She (*add*) that she (*look*) for an interesting job, and (*leave*) her previous one because she (*find*) the work (*bore*).

**2** Complete the phrasal verbs by putting in the missing particle. Choose from: *off, down, up, out.*

a   The escaped prisoner gave himself ......... to the police.
b   I must take ......... a driving licence.
c   The first edition of the book is completely sold .........
d   The doctor says that I'm run ......... and need a rest.
e   Do you think he'll carry ......... his threat?
f   We had to lay ......... several workers during the depression.
g   Call me ......... on Friday if the meeting is called .........
h   The teacher tried to cheer him .........
i   I'm fed ......... with this kind of work.
j   My dress is a little tight; it needs letting .........

**3** Put the following sentences into Direct Speech:
EXAMPLE:   He asked me where I was going, adding that he intended to stay indoors.
    Where are you going? I intend to stay indoors.

a   He asked Archie where he had bought his suit, adding that he liked it very much.
b   He said he was going to study Modern Art and asked me what I thought of the idea.
c   He asked me if I had been invited to the party and said that he was surprised that he hadn't been told about it.  *strange-*
d   He asked me whether I liked dancing, adding that he had been given two tickets for the ball the following evening.
e   He said he couldn't understand why I hadn't enjoyed the film, adding that he thought it was one of the best films he had seen for a long time.

36

f   He said that he was thinking of going to Paris for a holiday
and asked me whether I would like to join him.

**4**   Put in the missing relative pronoun. If it can be omitted, put it
in parentheses:
EXAMPLE: This is the person (whom, that) I met at the party.

a   The man ......... house was burgled has gone to the police. *[broke into]*

b   The police, in ......... I have great confidence, are trying to
find out ......... did it.

c   The man ......... you bought the house from is my uncle.

d   The River Thames, ......... flows through London, is more
than two hundred miles long.

e   The book ......... you lent me is very interesting.

f   My younger sister, ......... you spoke to at the meeting,
wants to study History.

g   I'm afraid that's all ......... I can tell you.

h   The girl ......... he is going to marry is an English teacher.

i   Brighton, ......... is fifty-two miles from London, is a
popular holiday resort. *[→ place.]*

j   This is the part of the river ......... I like to swim in.

**5**   Add question tags to the following:
EXAMPLE: He went home, didn't he?
He wasn't there, was he?

a   He is a very pleasant person, ......... ?

b   He won't be there, ......... ?

c   She shouldn't have gone alone, ......... ?

d   She ought to get up early, ......... ?

e   We have met before, ......... ?

f   He isn't very sure of himself, ......... ?

g   He must do it today, ......... ?

h   They'll be there early, ......... ?

i   He needs a haircut, ......... ?

**6**   The following words have been omitted from the paragraph.
Put them back in correct places:

| | | |
|---|---|---|
| alike | pedestrians | watch |
| killed | highways *national road* | injured |
| occur | providing | ever |

37

Hundreds of people are ...*2*.... on the road each year. Thousands more are seriously ..*8*..... The government can help us by ....*6*... money to improve the ...*5*...., but this is not enough. All who use the roads, ..*4*....., cyclists and motorists ...*10*., must be ...*9*..... on the ....*7*.... to see that accidents do not ..*3*.....

# PAPER 15

**1** Put the verbs in parentheses into a correct form:

a   It (*rain*) when we (*leave*); but by the time we (*get*) to the cinema, it (*stop*).

b   I (*not have*) a holiday since I (*come*) to London. I wish I (*take*) one last August.

c   My friend (*tell*) me that he (*go*) to the cinema and (*ask*) me whether I (*like*) (*go*) with him. When he (*tell*) me what film he (*go*) (*see*), I (*say*) that I already (*see*) it.

d   When he finally (*arrive*), we already (*wait*) more than an hour.

e   She (*not write*) to me since she (*change*) her address. When I (*hear*) from her, I (*get*) in touch with you.

f   I (*ask*) him whether I (*write*) to them. He (*tell*) me (*wait*) until the following week.

**2** Put in the missing prepositions:

a   I'm not acquainted ........ him.

b   You must try to adapt yourself ........ the different conditions.

c   I have no objection ........ helping people, but I don't like to be imposed ........

d   He's afraid ........ dogs.

e   The food here doesn't agree ........ me.

f   I sent it ........ airmail.

g   She is anxious ........ her health.

h   I have no appetite ........ work.

i   I don't like him ........ all.

j   I generally come ........ bus, but today I came ........ foot.

38

## 3 Infinitive and Gerund.

Put the verbs in parentheses into a correct form. Use an infinitive (with or without to), or a gerund:

EXAMPLE:  He promised (*finish*) (*write*) it before (*leave*).
          He promised to finish writing it before leaving.

a  He refused (*let*) me (*go*) on (*speak*).
b  I advise you (*wait*) before (*make*) a final decision.
c  It's no use (*ask*) him. He can't help you (*find*) it.
d  Please make him (*stop*) (*sing*). I thought he had finished (*take*) music lessons long ago.
e  Do you remember (*meet*) me before?
f  If a thing is worth (*do*), it's worth (*do*) well.
g  Please try (*avoid*) (*drive*) at night.
h  'I usually go by train.' 'Try (*go*) by bus for a change.'
i  Did you remember (*post*) the letter I gave you?
j  I can't afford (*buy*) a new car without first (*sell*) my old one.

## 4  Fill in the blank spaces with one of the following:
*except that, yet, therefore, since, in spite of, in case, however hard, except, because of, so that.*

a  They decided to go out ......... the bad weather.
b  He's stupid and arrogant, ......... some people like him.
c  I know nothing about him ......... he was born in Leeds.
d  He will not pass the test ......... he tries.
e  She sent her daughter to England ......... she might learn English quickly.
f  We missed the bus, ......... we had to take a taxi.
g  I come here every day ......... Saturday.
h  We stayed at home ......... the bad weather.
i  ......... the weather was bad, we decided not to go out.
j  Take an umbrella ......... it rains.

## 5  Complete the following questions and then answer each question with a complete sentence. Begin each answer with either *I don't know*, or *I've no idea*.
EXAMPLE: 'How old is John?' 'I've no idea how old he is.'

a  How high .........?        b  How far .........?
c  How much .........?        d  How many .........?

e   How often .........?          f   What time .........?
g   How long .........?           h   How soon .........?
i   How wide .........?           j   How deep .........?
k   How big .........?            l   How quickly .........?

**6** Write sentences to show clearly the difference between the two words in each of the following pairs:

| diary | rare | tasty | sew | dress (verb) |
| dairy | scarce | tasteful | sow | wear (verb) |

# PAPER 16

**1** Put the verbs in parentheses into a correct form. Pay attention to word order:

My brother still (*sleep*) when I (*get*) up this morning. After I (*shake*) him three or four times, he finally (*open*) his eyes and (*ask*) what the time (*be*). (*See*) that there (*be*) very little time left, he (*get*) (*dress*) as quickly as he (*can*). If he (*not do*) so, he certainly (*be*) late for school. This only (*happen*) once since the new school year (*begin*).

**2** Fill in the blank spaces with one of the following groups. Pay attention to the tense form of the verb:

| fall out with | cash in on | go through with | get on with |
| go in for | live up to | get on for | run out of |

a   A person should ......... his principles.
b   I don't want to ......... him over a little thing like that.
c   I am determined to ......... my original plan.
d   Some shopkeepers are ......... the present shortage of fruit.
e   My son has decided to ......... stamp collecting.
f   How old is he? He must be ......... forty.
g   He doesn't ......... the other clerks in the office.
h   I've ......... sugar. Please get me some when you go shopping.

**3** Complete the following sentences by using the correct form of the words in parentheses:

a  (*eloquence*) He spoke very ..........
b  (*defend*) This is a .......... weapon.
c  (*argue*) The .......... lasted quite a long time.
d  (*relieve*) She gave a sigh of .......... when he finally left.
e  (*attend*) The audience was very .......... during the lecture.
f  (*grave*) You don't realize the .......... of the situation.
g  (*broad*) Travel .......... the mind.
h  (*deceive*) Appearances are often ..........
i  (*create*) Children should be encouraged to be ..........
j  (*snob*) He behaved very ..........


**4**  Put the adverb in brackets in the correct place in the sentence:

a  I go out at night. (*seldom*)
b  I do my homework in the afternoon. (*generally*)
c  I speak French in the class. (*never*)
d  He is late. (*hardly ever*)
e  We have finished the book. (*almost*)
f  You must come on time. (*always*)
g  You can tell what he is thinking. (*never, really*)
h  He is at home. (*hardly ever*)
i  Have you seen him angry? (*ever*)
j  He hasn't finished the book. (*still*)


**5  Clauses of Concession.**
Complete the following sentences in any suitable way:

a  Although she spends a lot of money on clothes, she ..........
b  However hard I try, I ..........
c  In spite of the fact that he doesn't work hard, he ..........
d  Although he is over seventy, he ..........
e  He .......... even though he has never been to England.
f  Although he is a very busy man, ..........
g  He .......... in spite of the fact that I told him not to.
h  However much he earns, ..........
i  .......... although the food was very good.
j  Even if he apologizes, I ..........
k  Though he doesn't earn much money, he ..........
l  Although I hadn't seen him for twenty years, I ..........
m  He ..........; he didn't, though.
n  He ..........; he can't, though.

6  Write sentences to show that the following nouns may be countable or uncountable:

*dress, power, hair, weakness, industry, fire.*

EXAMPLE: I have two new *dresses*. (Countable)

Women usually pay more attention to *dress* than men do. (Uncountable)


# PAPER 17

**1** Put the verbs in brackets into a correct tense.  Suggest two possibilities for each sentence:

a  I (*teach*) English since 1950.

b  I'll have a drink when I (*finish*) my work.

c  When I came home, the children (*eat*) dinner.

d  He (*read*) the *Daily Telegraph* now.

e  I told him what I (*do*).

f  I thought he (*like*) it.

g  By the time we (*get*) to the station, the train (*leave*).

h  Where he (*live*) now?

i  Where you (*go*) tomorrow?

j  He just (*go*) out when I arrived.


**2**  Put in the missing prepositions:

a  I sometimes confuse adjectives ......... adverbs.

b  He has recovered ......... his illness.

c  He arrived ......... the station ......... 9 o'clock.

d  Wait ......... me. I'll be ready ......... ten minutes.

e  I prefer the theatre ......... the cinema.

f  I objected ......... the noise they were making.

g  The workers have gone ......... strike.

h  Please forgive me ......... not arriving ......... time ......... the lesson.

i  It is the chance ........ a lifetime.

j  The books should arrive any day. They've been ......... order ......... several weeks.

**3** Write sentences to which the following tags could be added:

EXAMPLE: You weren't there, were you?

He went home, didn't he?

a ........., mustn't we?  b ........., does he?

c ........., shouldn't they?  d ........., is he?

e ........., do you?  f ........., did you?

g ........., did he?  h ........., can't you?

i ........., won't they?  j ........., will you?

**4** Put in the missing relative pronoun. If it can be omitted, put it in parentheses:

a My father, ......... you met the other day, thinks you have a lot of talent.

b All the people ......... know him think very highly of him.

c Bridge, ......... I play at least once a week, is a fascinating game.

d Is he the person ......... you were speaking about?

e Any manager ......... did a thing like that wouldn't keep his job very long.

f Somerset Maugham, ......... stories I enjoy very much, died a few years ago.

g This refrigerator, ......... I have had for over ten years, has never given me any trouble.

h He did very well in the examination, ......... surprised me very much.

i Would you please return the book ......... I lent you last week?

j The boy ......... I was speaking to is a very good athlete.

**5** Complete the following sentences with a suitable form of *rise*, *raise* or *arise*:

a Please ......... your voice. I can't hear you.

b Yeast makes bread .........

c He never fails to ......... his hat to me.

d The curtain ......... at 7 o'clock every evening.

e It's quite difficult to ......... a family properly.

f The price of bread has ......... recently.

g How did the quarrel .........?

h Do you know where the Thames .........?

i Some new difficulties have recently ........
j If you know the answer, please ........ your hand.
k The sun ........ in the east.
l We are trying to ........ money for the new hospital.

**6** Put the adverbs and adverbial phrases in the correct places in the sentence. In some cases there is more than one possibility:

a I would prefer to go alone. (*very much*)
b I haven't seen him. (*recently*)
c He sang. (*last night, very well, at the concert*)
d The lights went out. (*suddenly*)
e I have enough time to finish the work. (*barely*)
f Does he come to see you? (*ever*)
g You must all work. (*quietly, in the laboratory, this afternoon*)
h He comes to see me. (*often*)
i He hasn't done it. (*yet*)
j I have spoken to him. (*already*)

# PAPER 18

**1** Put the verbs in brackets into a correct form. Pay attention to word order:

a I (*not receive*) a letter from Pauline since she left England. René (*tell*) me that she already (*write*) to her and (*wait*) for a reply. She (*say*) she (*let*) me (*know*) as soon as she (*hear*) from her. I really (*like*) (*know*) how she (*get*) on.
b John just (*go*) out when I (*call*) at his house. His mother (*say*) she (*be*) sure he (*not be*) long and (*ask*) me (*wait*) for him. (*Not have*) anything special (*do*), I (*decide*) (*wait*) until eight o'clock and if he (*not return*) by then, I (*leave*). I (*not be*) there ten minutes when John (*arrive*), (*delight*) (*find*) me (*wait*) for him.

**2** Complete the phrasal verbs by putting in the missing particles. Choose from:

*up, into, away, out, down, over.*

a   If war breaks ........., most of us will be called .........
b   You go on; I'll catch you .........
c   The weather is bad at present. I hope it will soon clear
    .........
d   He was offered a very good job but he turned it .........
e   Will you please look ......... my letter to see if I have made
    any mistakes.
f   She broke ......... when she heard the terrible news.
g   I wouldn't sell my old clothes. I'd rather give them .........
h   If I don't know the meaning of a word, I look it ......... in
    the dictionary.
i   I'll think it ......... and give you my answer tomorrow.
j   He came ......... a fortune when his uncle passed
    .........

3   Put the verbs in brackets into a correct form:

a   If he (*invite*) me earlier, I (*may go*).
b   I (*do*) it if I (*be*) you.
c   (*Not do*) it unless you (*have*) to.
d   Thank goodness it's all over. I (*never begin*) it if I (*know*) it
    was going to take me so long.
e   If the dress (*fit*) me, I (*buy*) it. (Three possibilities)
f   Had you warned me, I (*be*) more careful.
g   (*Take*) an umbrella if you (*not want*) to get wet.
h   If he hasn't done his homework, the teacher (*be*) angry.
i   If he (*continue*) to work hard, he (*do*) well in next week's
    examination.
j   If I (*be*) ten years younger, I (*change*) my profession.

4   Complete the following sentences in any suitable way:

a   Although he ........., I .........
b   It was such a ......... that he .........
c   The box was so ......... that nobody could .........
d   He read the story slowly so that .........
e   Either John or Mary ......... going to .........
f   I met him while .........
g   I will not do it until .........
h   Fortunately for me, .........

i   He seldom .........; however, he .........
j   The exercises were difficult, yet ........

**5**  Write questions or statements to which the following could be responses:

a  No, why should I?           b  Bernard Shaw did.
c  None of us can.             d  About two thousand miles.
e  Yes, I had to.              f  I hope not.
g  Not if I can avoid it.      h  I sincerely hope so.
i  Spanish is.                 j  Are you crazy?

**6**  Idioms for class discussion and paraphrase:

a  to break a record.
b  the rush hour.
c  to be tongue-tied.
d  to be thin-skinned.
e  to let someone down.
f  to feel blue.
g  to shake off a cold.
h  to catch someone red-handed.

# PAPER 19

**1**  Put the verbs in brackets into a correct form. Pay attention to word order:

Henry only just (*leave*) when his mother (*call*) and (*ask*) whether she (*can*) (*speak*) to him. When I (*tell*) her that he already (*leave*), she (*ask*) whether he (*take*) a taxi. When I (*ask*) her why she (*be*) so worried about him, she (*say*) he (*not feel*) well lately, adding that the doctor (*advise*) him (*not work*) so hard. While we (*speak*), she (*ask*) me if I (*go*) anywhere the following evening. When I (*tell*) her I (*not be*), she (*invite*) me for dinner, (*say*) that I (*can*) (*bring*) a friend if I (*want*) to.

**2**  Put in the missing prepositions:

a  We are related ........ marriage.
b  He is married ........ my cousin.

c I've decided ......... going alone. I wouldn't enjoy it.
d He's the kind ......... person you can safely confide ..........
e I have very little opportunity ......... speaking English.
f We are confident ......... success.
g He dived ......... the water ......... the top board.
h This is an exception ......... the rule.
i They promised to abide ......... your decision.
j He is absorbed ......... his work.

**3** Make additions to the following statements:
EXAMPLE: John didn't go. *Neither/nor* did the others.
My sister lives in Glasgow. *So* does my uncle.

a Shaw wrote many plays.
b February is a cold month.
c Potatoes aren't expensive now.
d Oranges keep you healthy.
e I shan't be here tomorrow.
f Mary can drive.
g I must stay at home tonight.
h John hasn't had a letter for several weeks.
i Byron was an English poet.
j You shouldn't smoke so much.

**4** Rewrite the following sentences in the Passive Voice. Use 'by' only when you think it is really necessary.

a Columbus discovered America.
b Nobody ever does anything in this office.
c People say the new film is excellent.
d They were repairing it when I arrived.
e They have already signed the contract.
f Dr. Brown will deliver the lecture.
g Nobody has told me where to go.
h We shall finish the work tomorrow.
i They think he is a wealthy man.
j You ought to do it as soon as possible.

**5** Complete the following sentences by using the correct form of the word in parentheses:

a  (*merchant*) We export our ......... to many countries.
b  (*marvel*) It's a ......... opportunity for me.
c  (*method*) He works very .........
d  (*signify*) Do you attach any ......... to his remarks?
e  (*able, promote*) His ......... to speak English well makes it very difficult for him to get .........
f  (*fortune*) ........., I didn't have to answer all the questions.
g  (*obstinate*) I was surprised at his .........
h  (*day*) I should like to know your ......... programme.
i  (*monotony*) He has a very ......... voice.
j  (*pay*) We have two more ......... to make on our television set.

**6**  Write sentences to show clearly the difference between the two words in each of the following pairs:

| course | hung | storey | born | human |
|--------|------|--------|------|-------|
| coarse | hanged | story | borne | humane |

# PAPER 20

**1**  Put the verbs in parentheses into a correct form.

While I (*sit*) in the library one day, I (*meet*) an old friend whom I (*not see*) for quite a long time. When I (*ask*) him how he (*get*) along, he (*tell*) me that he (*work*) in a garage, but seriously (*think*) of (*give*) up the job because he (*not like*) the people (*work*) there. He (*add*) that he (*consider*) (*go*) abroad for a while. I (*tell*) him that I (*think*) it (*be*) a good idea. On (*leave*), I (*ask*) him for his telephone number, (*say*) I (*call*) him if I (*hear*) of anything that (*may*) be of interest to him.

**2**  Complete the phrasal verbs by putting in the missing particle. Choose from:
   *after, off, for, over, out, on, up, round.*

a  He takes ......... his father in many ways.
b  I cannot give you an answer till I have talked it ......... with my wife.

48

c His new book is coming ........ next month.
d What do the letters G.B.S. stand ........ ?
e The aeroplane took ......... at 6 o'clock.
f Quite a lot of people are coming. I hope there will be enough chairs to go ........
g She likes to show ........ when she is in company.
h Please bring the matter ........ at the next meeting.
i Next year I shall take ........ golf.
j You have to work hard if you want to get ........ in life.

**3** Write sentences to which the following might be responses:
EXAMPLES: Mary was here yesterday. So was I.
   John can't swim. Neither can his sister.

a ........ So must I.
b ........ Neither does his brother.
c ........ So does John.
d ........ Neither should you.
e ........ So will the rest of us.
f ........ So ought you.
g ........ Neither did the others.
h ........ So can she.
i ........ Neither do we.
j ........ Neither have we.

**4** Put the following sentences into Direct Speech:

a He told me not to smoke in there if I didn't want to get into trouble.
b He said he might go to Europe for his holidays, adding that it depended on his financial situation.
c He asked me why I didn't work harder, and said I would regret it later.
d He said that he had to be back before midnight because he hadn't got a key.
e She told me she could never remember where she put her glasses, and said that it was driving her crazy.
f He told me to be there before 6 o'clock, saying that I should take a taxi if I had to.
g He said he was sure we had met before and asked me whether I have ever been to Rome.

h He asked me whether I was going and I said I was.

i He asked me whether he should post the letter.

j He begged me not to tell anybody what had happened.

**5** Writing questions or statements to which the following could be responses:

a I know. I'm looking forward to it.

b Four of us did.

c About three days ago.

d Since 1960.

e The green one, please.

f No, I'd rather go alone.

g As soon as I can.

h I didn't think much of it.

i Tomorrow, I think.

j Oranges are.

**6** The following words have been omitted from the paragraph. Put them back in the correct places:

| even | requires | harmful | perfect |
|------|----------|---------|---------|
| state | concern | larder | family |
| germs | health | particularly | tainted |

As a housewife, the safety of the ........ is your first ........
This includes safety in the home and ........, safeguarding
their ........ by serving them clean hygienic food. ........
when it has come into the house in a hygienic ........, food
can easily become ........ through bad storage. Food is a
........ breeding ground for ........ and ........
bacteria. Good food ........ a clean, carefully planned, well-
organized ........

# PAPER 21

**1** Put the verbs in parentheses into a correct form:

When I (*tell*) my teacher that I (*have*) a little difficulty with conditional sentences at the moment, he (*ask*) me (*come*) and (*see*)
him the following afternoon. After he (*give*) me a brief explana-

tion, he (*ask*) me several questions and then (*give*) me a short written test. I (*be delighted*) (*find*) that I (*not make*) a single mistake. While we (*speak*), his wife (*enter*) and (*ask*) me whether I (*like*) something (*drink*). It (*be*) possible that if I (*not go*) (*see*) my teacher yesterday, I (*may fail*) in yesterday's test. Although our papers (*not yet be returned*) to us, I (*have*) nothing (*worry*) about. My teacher (*tell*) me a few minutes ago that I (*do*) very well.

**2** Put in the missing prepositions:

a   He was absent ......... class.
b   He was told to abstain ......... alcohol.
c   She broke it ......... accident; she didn't do it .........
    purpose.
d   According ......... the radio, it will be fine tomorrow.
e   I cannot account ......... his strange behaviour.
f   I am acting ......... the headmaster ......... his absence.
g   We must take his age ......... account.
h   I can't get accustomed ......... driving ......... the left
    side ......... the road.
i   What he said doesn't apply ......... me.
j   I don't approve ......... children going to bed late.

**3** Complete the following sentences in any suitable way:

a   If you had told me earlier, .........
b   What would you do if ......... ?
c   If she doesn't apologize, I .........
d   I ......... unless I leave immediately.
e   She would never have spoken to me again if .........
f   Hide it quickly if .........
g   She would have bought the dog if .........
h   If I had the courage, I .........
i   If I am tired, I am not able to .........
j   She won't be able to do it unless .........

**4** Replace '*although*' with '*in spite of*' and make any other necessary changes:
EXAMPLE: Although it is cold, she is not wearing a coat.
          In spite of the cold weather, she is not wearing a coat.

a   Although the price was high, she decided to buy it.
b   Although his parents objected, he went to live in Italy.
c   Although it was difficult, I managed to pass the test.
d   Although his friends helped him, he failed in the test.
e   Although he is an old man, he can read without glasses.
f   Although he was hungry, he couldn't eat the food.
g   Although he has a bad memory, he is a good student.
h   Although the handwriting was bad, I was able to read it.
i   Although the journey was tiring, I enjoyed the trip very much.
j   Although his lecture was a long one, nobody lost interest.

**5**  Put the correct form of the verb *to lie* or *to lay*:

| lie | lied | lied | lying |
|-----|------|------|-------|
| lie | lay  | lain | lying |
| lay | laid | laid | laying |

a   A waiter must know how to ........ a table.
b   I was ........ in bed when the doctor arrived.
c   '........ down for an hour every afternoon,' said the doctor.
d   How long has that book been ........ there?
e   How many eggs do your hens ........ every week?
f   He was ........ when he said that.
g   ........ the baby down very gently.
h   Don't you dare ........ a finger on him.
i   I ........ in bed all yesterday afternoon.
j   If you do that, you'll be ........ yourself open to criticism.
k   I wouldn't ........ my hopes on him if I were you.
l   I saw him ........ on the grass enjoying the sunshine.

**6**  Idioms for class discussion and paraphrase:

a   To make hay while the sun shines. take advantage of
b   To take a busman's holiday: to work during the hol. at an othe
c   To put the cart before the horse: put the wrong thing first.
d   To tell a white lie: tell a lie that helps –
e   A white elephant: have a real burden –
f   To have a good mind to do something: to be strongly willin
g   To turn over a new leaf: αρχίζω κανούργια ζωή.
h   To be green: άγγιχ, jealous –

52

# PAPER 22

**1**  Put the verbs in parentheses into a correct form. Pay attention to word order:

I (*arrive*) rather late and (*find*) that the party already (*begin*). Some couples (*dance*) while others just (*talk*). One girl (*look*) into the mirror and (*comb*) her hair. Suddenly I (*see*) who it (*be*). It (*be*) somebody I (*meet*) in Europe last summer. (*Think*) I (*surprise*) her, I (*go*) over and (*touch*) her on the shoulder. When she (*turn*) round, I (*realize*) I never (*meet*) the girl before. After (*apologize*), I (*ask*) her whether she (*like*) (*dance*). It (*turn*) out that she (*be*) an excellent dancer, besides (*be*) a highly intelligent person. As a result, I (*have*) a very enjoyable evening.

**2**  Complete the phrasal verbs by putting in the missing particle. Choose from:

*up, off, in, out, round, over.*

a  Ask him ......... Don't let him stand at the door.
b  Take care that the milk does not boil .........
c  Bring your friend ......... this evening.
d  Hurry ......... or we shall be late.
e  The car drew ......... outside the bank and two men got .........
f  Please drop ......... whenever you are in the neighbour-hood.
g  She suddenly burst ......... laughing.
h  We shall have to call ......... a doctor if his condition doesn't improve.
i  Although he was absent for a week, he soon caught ......... with the other students.
j  One or two students dropped ......... during the dull lecture. In fact, one began snoring and I had to wake him .........

**3**  Put in the missing relative pronoun. If it can be omitted, put it in parentheses:

EXAMPLE: I've told you all (*that*) I know.

a  The girl ......... you are speaking about is my cousin.
b  The student ......... book you borrowed wants it back.

53

c  Mr. Bridges, ......... gave us a very interesting lecture last month, will be here again tomorrow.

d  I did all ......... was necessary to be done.

e  The fish ......... they serve in that restaurant is excellent.

f  Cricket, ......... is a very popular sport in England, is unknown in many countries.

g  The person ......... wrote this article doesn't know his subject.

h  Salmon, ......... we had for dinner last night, is very expensive at this time of the year.

i  My employer, ......... you met yesterday, is an excellent tennis player.

j  Is this the book ......... you were looking for?


**4** Complete the following sentences by using the correct form of the words in parentheses:

a  (*react*) I was surprised at his .........

b  (*reluctance*) He went very .........

c  (*invent*) He has a very ......... mind.

d  (*origin*) The ......... plan was better than this one.

e  (*recognize*) ......... was impossible in such darkness.

f  (*solve*) I didn't realize that the ......... was so simple.

g  (*notice*) His influence on her is quite ...:......

h  (*hesitate*) Why are you so .........?

i  (*explain*) I am waiting for an .........

j  (*critic, destroy*) I'm not interested in hearing your .........; it's always .........


**5** Put the verbs in parentheses into the correct form. Use an infinitive (with or without to), a gerund or a present participle. Note: Both gerunds and present participles have the same form:

a  It's no good (*ask*) me. You'd better (*try*) someone else.

b  I advised him (*go*) to the police. John suggested (*offer*) a reward.

c  It's not much use (*have*) a bicycle if you are inclined (*be*) nervous about (*ride*) in traffic.

d  I caught him (*read*) my letters. Fancy him (*do*) a thing like that!

e  I can't make him (*do*) his homework. I've threatened (*punish*)

54

him, but it doesn't help.
f  I prefer (*read*) a book to (*sit*) in a café.
g  Something always prevents me from (*read*) the newspaper. I can never finish a page without (*be*) interrupted.
h  I found him (*sit*) on a chair (*cry*) bitterly.
i  Practise (*read*) aloud. It may help you (*improve*) your pronunciation.
j  He was made (*write*) it again.

6  Write sentences to show that the following words may be countable or uncountable:
*success, iron, cheese, cake, crime, glass.*
EXAMPLE: *Crime* doesn't pay. (Uncountable)
He committed a *crime* (Countable)

# PAPER 23

1  Put the verbs in brackets into a correct form. Pay attention to word order:

It (*rain*) very heavily when I (*get*) up this morning. I (*think*) it never (*stop*), and I (*begin*) (*wonder*) how I (*go*) (*get*) to work. Luckily, as I (*eat*) breakfast, it suddenly (*stop*) (*rain*) and the sun (*begin*) (*shine*). If the rain (*continue*) I never (*get*) to work on time. I (*work*) for the same firm for over two years and I don't remember ever (*be*) late. This may have something (*do*) with the fact that I (*be promoted*) twice in the last two years.

2  Put in the missing prepositions:

a  He's ashamed ........ himself.
b  He's an authority ........ this subject.
c  You have no authority ........ me.
d  Are you aware ........ the danger?
e  Taxation is usually based ........ income.
f  His silence is an admission ........ guilt.
g  I wonder what became ........ John.
h  He began ........ telling a story.

i He begged ........ forgiveness.

j I don't believe ........ miracles.

## 3 Clauses of Result.

Complete the following sentences in any suitable way:

a It was such a hot day that ........

b He speaks so quickly that ........

c His handwriting is so bad that ........

d He is such an interesting speaker that ........

e The sea was so rough that ........

f I was so tired that ........

g He is such a reckless driver that ........

h His eyesight is so bad that ........

i He is such a generous person that ........

j It was such a boring evening that ........

k The weather was so bad that ........

l He had drunk so much liquor at the party that ........


**4** Put the following sentences into the Active Voice. Choose any suitable subject where one is not provided:

EXAMPLE: Where was the money found?

Where did he find the money?

a What were you told to do?

b They were made to learn the poem by heart.

c The house was being cleaned while the dinner was being cooked.

d It must have been done by an artist.

e The business has been taken over by his competitors.

f Such customs should be done away with.

g Why haven't the letters been written?

h It must be done at once.

i I ought to have been told sooner.

j I wasn't told that he had been dismissed.


**5** Put the following sentences into Direct Speech:

EXAMPLE: He said (*that*) he didn't want to go.

'I don't want to go.'

a He asked me to wait till he came.

b He said he would be able to go.

56

c He told me that he couldn't hear what I was saying.

d He told me that they had never had such a wonderful holiday.

e She said that she might come on foot, explaining that it depended on the weather.

f She told her mother that she had to go out, adding that she wouldn't be back before midnight. She asked her not to worry if she was a little late.

g He said he would go if he had time.

h He said that if we were late, we might not be able to get in.

i She wondered whether they would ever meet again.

j He said he would help me if it was necessary.

**6** For each word in this list, find another that is pronounced the same but spelt differently:

EXAMPLE: sea, see; two, too:

| heard | wait | hour | red | seen | heir |
|-------|------|------|-----|------|------|
| heel | been | made | lain | tied | fair |

# PAPER 24

**1** Put the verbs in parentheses into a correct form. Use the Passive Voice only:

a The room (*not clean*) since last week.

b The room (*still clean*) when I arrived.

c If he (*find*) guilty, he (*send*) to prison. (Three possibilities)

d It should (*do*) a long time ago.

e Why I (*not tell*) about this yesterday?

f It must (*take*) while I was out.

g When the house (*paint*), it will look different. (Two possibilities)

h Nothing (*do*) since he (*take*) to hospital.

i By the time we arrived, the children (*put*) to bed.

j I expect you (*interest*) in everything that (*do*) here.

**2** Complete the phrasal verbs by putting in the missing particle. Choose from:

*through, up, out, in, down.*

a   He read ......... the names on the list.

b   Darkness had set ......... long before we reached home.

c   He made ......... the whole story; I don't believe a word of it.

d   The shoes I bought last year are already worn .........

e   Two masked men held ......... the cashier.

f   I'm determined to see the matter ......... I'm not giving ......... at this stage.

g   Two teams have dropped ......... of the competition.

h   He would lay ......... his life for his country.

i   Can you pick me ......... on this photograph?

j   We'll pick you ......... at 9 o'clock. Please be ready.

## 3   Inversion of Subject and Verb.

Rewrite the following sentences, putting the words in parentheses at the beginning and making the necessary changes:

EXAMPLES: The lesson had hardly begun when the lights went out. (*Hardly*)

Hardly had the lesson begun when the lights went out.

It can't be done in any other way. (*in no other way*)
In no other way can it be done.

a   They had never seen such a sight before. (*Never before*)

b   They had no sooner entered the theatre than the performance began. (*No sooner*)

c   I will not do such a thing under any circumstances. (*Under no circumstances*)

d   The lesson will not begin until everyone is seated. (*Not until*)

e   I will on no account sign this document. (*On no account*)

f   He wrote the letter so badly that I couldn't read it. (*So badly*)

g   You will succeed only by working hard. (*Only*)

h   He seldom takes a holiday. (*Seldom*)

i   He not only advised me what to do; he also lent me the money. (*Not only*)

j   He little realizes how ill he is. (*Little*)

k   The old man didn't say a word. (*Not a word*)

l   The soldiers didn't utter a sound while the general was speaking. (*Not a sound*)

m   I have hardly ever seen anyone so unhappy. (*Hardly ever*) n   I have rarely seen such a beautiful sunset. (*Rarely*)

o   He didn't speak to us even once. (*Not even once*)


**4**  Put in the missing words. Use *some* or *any* or a compound word beginning with *some* or *any* (e.g. *something, somebody, anything*, etc.):

a   If ......... calls while I am out, tell him I had to go .........

b   I left my book ......... in this room. Has ......... seen it?

c   Can't ......... help you? I'm sure ......... can.

d   ......... has got to do it; ........., that's what he said.

e   You can tell ......... you like. It's not a secret.

f   If you really need ......... cigarettes, I'll go and get .........

g   Hardly ......... noticed that ......... was missing.

h   Would you like to go ......... tonight? I'm sure you would.

i   ......... day I'll tell you what really happened.

j   Is there ......... I can do to help? I'm sorry but there isn't ......... here who can really do ......... about it.


**5**  Write sentences to which the following tags could be added:

EXAMPLE: You didn't go, did you?

You've been there, haven't you?

a   ........., aren't there?

b   ........., wasn't it?

c   ........., need we?

d   ........., shall we?

e   ........., oughtn't you?

f   ........., is it?

g   ........., were there?

h   ........., couldn't you?

i   ........., will he?

j   ........., will there?


**6**  Write sentences to show the difference between the two words in each of the following pairs:

| die | except | flowed | older | success |
|-----|--------|--------|-------|---------|
| dye | besides | flown | elder | succession |

59

# PAPER 25

**1** Put the verbs in parentheses into a suitable form. Pay attention to word order:

When this course (*end*), I (*be*) here for nine months. The last three months (*pass*) very quickly. If I (*do*) well in the final examination, I (*try*) (*get*) a job here. I (*like*) (*stay*) for another year. I then (*have*) an opportunity (*improve*) my spoken English. If I (*do*) that, I (*have*) no difficulty in (*get*) a good job when I (*return*) to my own country.

**2** Put in the missing prepositions:

a  I never bet ......... horses.
b  We usually benefit ......... experience.
c  Beware ......... talking ......... strangers.
d  You can't blame him ......... that.
e  He always puts the blame ......... me.
f  Many people are blind ......... their own faults.
g  I borrowed the money ......... John and lent it .........
   my brother.
h  He boasts ......... his ability to analyse handwriting.
i  Are you insured ......... fire?
j  Don't interfere ......... them. Leave them alone.

**3** Idioms for class discussion and paraphrase:

a  Down tools.
b  Hold one's own.
c  Lose one's temper.
d  Keep a straight face.
e  Strike while the iron's hot.
f  Have the time of one's life.
g  Hitch-hike.
h  Cut it fine.

**4** **Unreal Past**
Study the following examples carefully:

1  I am sorry I can't go = I wish I could go.
2  I am sorry he isn't here = I wish he were here.

**60**

3  I am sorry I bought it = I wish I hadn't bought it.
4  She is sorry she went = She wishes she hadn't gone.

Other expressions: *It's time*, *if only*, *suppose*, *I'd rather*. Now put the verbs in parentheses into the correct tense.

a  I wish I (*know*) English better.
b  I wish I (*be*) younger.
c  I wish you (*tell*) me earlier.
d  Shall I go now? I'd rather you (*go*) tomorrow.
e  It's time the children (*be*) in bed.
f  I wish I (*work*) harder when I was at school.
g  I can't go out now. Suppose the boss (*walk*) in!
h  It's time you (*have*) a haircut.
i  I wish I (*have*) a bigger breakfast. Now I'm hungry.
j  If only I (*know*) earlier!
k  I wish I (*can*) drive a car.
l  I wish I (*not tell*) him. Now everyone will know.

**5**  Complete the following sentences by using the correct form of the words in parentheses:

a  (*irritate*) Why are you so ........ today?
b  (*injure*) It wasn't a serious ........
c  (*angry*) There was a note of ........ in his voice.
d  (*obey*) He is a very ........ child; he never ........ me.
e  (*hero*) He behaved ........ In fact, he got a medal for
   ........
f  (*enthuse*) He showed very little ........ for my plan.
g  (*apply*) We have already received twenty ........ for the job and ten of the ........ are under thirty.
h  (*friend*) I was very much impressed by the ........ of the local population.
i  (*friend*) Nations must learn to live together in ........
j  (*friend*) He ........ me when I first came to this country.

**6**  The following words have been omitted from the paragraph. Put them back in the correct places:

| | | |
|---|---|---|
| preserve | canned | particularly |
| various | barrels | packed |
| fast | types | customary |

61

......... species of fish, especially the smaller ........., are
......... in oil or tomato for export. Others are dried, salted,
and ......... in boxes and ......... or smoked to .........
them. Exports of fish go ......... to Germany and to Catholic
countries of southern Europe, where the eating of fish on
......... days is .........

# PAPER 26

**1** Put the verbs in parentheses into a correct tense. Suggest a
sensible alternative wherever possible:

a By the time we (*arrive*), the film (*start*).
b As soon as I (*finish*) what I (*do*), I'll go to bed.
c I (*wait*) for more *than an hour when* he finally (*arrive*).
d I just (*speak*) to Gerda. She (*tell*) me she (*leave*) for Vienna on Friday.
e Nothing (*change*) since you (*leave*).
f In another ten minutes we (*sit*) here for exactly two hours.
g It's time I (*be*) able to do this work.
h I (*see*) him last week, but I (*not see*) him since.
i I (*see*) him now. He (*talk*) to John. I (*wonder*) what they (*talk*) about. It (*be*) more than a year since they (*see*) each other.
j You (*not wish*) you (*have*) a Rolls-Royce?

**2** Complete the phrasal verb by adding the missing particle.
Choose from:

*off, through, up, out, in.*

a I'm sure he will soon turn ......... He is seldom late.
b Let's roll ......... our sleeves and start work.
c The doctor feels sure that the patient will pull .........
d The liquid gave ......... a peculiar odour.
e I'll come to the airport to see you .........
f I think I'll take a week ......... I need a holiday.
g It'll take me a few days to run ......... my new car.
h The mystery has finally been cleared .........
i We shall camp ......... in the forest tonight.
j The students were told ......... for being late.

62

3. Complete the following sentences in any suitable way:

a  If ........., I would have done it.
b  I won't go unless .........
c  If he were here now, he .........
d  If ........., she would be very happy.
e  They ......... if the price hadn't been so high.
f  If there is time, I .........
g  Do it yourself if .........
h  If he ........., I might buy it.
i  If ........., I would have to go.
j  The crop will be ruined unless .........

## 4  Causative Form.

Complete the following sentences by supplying the correct form of the verb *to have* or *to get* and a suitable past participle:

EXAMPLES: We should get our groceries delivered.
          I am going to have a suit made in London.
          I had my eyesight tested.

a  I ......... my watch ......... last week.
b  My trousers are too long. I must ......... them .........
c  Her skirt is too short. She is going ......... it .........
d  I ......... my piano ......... once a year.
e  It's time I ......... my hair .........
f  This suit is dirty. I must ......... it .........
g  Tell the secretary ......... six copies .........
h  I must ......... my shoes .........
i  I ......... the house ......... last year.
j  I ......... my knives ......... once a year.

## 5  Clauses of Purpose

EXAMPLE: The teacher told the students to read the story two
         or three times *so that* they might know it well.

Complete the following sentences in any suitable way:

a  The parents spoke French so that the children .........
b  He sent his daughter to Paris so that she .........
c  I took a taxi in order to .........
d  He spoke clearly and slowly so that .........
e  Take an umbrella in case it .........

f I went early so as to ………

g He sat in the first row so that he ………

h ……… so that it should be a surprise.

i ……… so that he might not forget it.

j ……… so that he might do well in the examination.

k ……… so as not to wake the children.

l ……… in order not to attract attention.

m ……… so that he wouldn't forget.

n ……… so that they would get a good view.

**6** Write sentences to show the difference between the two words in each of the following pairs:

| | | | | |
|---|---|---|---|---|
| spend | occasion | effort | alert | decent |
| waste | opportunity | afford | aware | descent |

# PAPER 27

**1** Put the verbs in parentheses into a correct form. Pay attention to word order:

Suzanne (*come*) in a few minutes ago (*look*) as if she (*see*) a ghost. She (*tell*) me what (*happen*). 'I (*walk*) along the street,' she said, 'when I (*approach*) by someone who (*ask*) me what the time (*be*). On (*hear*) him (*speak*), I (*have*) the feeling that we (*meet*) before. After we (*speak*) for some time, I (*discover*) that the person (*be*) none other than my younger brother, who I (*think*) (*die*) during the war. If he (*not speak*) to me, it is probable that we (*may never learn*) of each other's existence.

**2** Put in the missing prepositions:

a He's going ……… business when he leaves school.

b Please call ……… me when you are in the neighbourhood.

c He's not capable ……… such a thing.

d I don't care ……… modern music.

e That's characteristic ……… him.

f Does this ship call ……… Venice?

g They called ……… Mr. Jones to make a speech.

h Please take care ……… the baby while I am out.

i   Switzerland is famous ......... its beautiful scenery.
j   I'm ......... charge ......... the factory while the manager
    is away.


**3** Put in the missing relative pronouns and commas: (in this
exercise none of them can be omitted):

a   The Tower of London ......... we visited last week is more
    than nine hundred years old.
b   Vienna ......... is the capital of Austria is a very beautiful
    city.
c   My younger brother ......... got married last week is
    thinking of going to Australia.
d   Margaret and Jack in ......... house we are making the
    party are a very charming couple.
e   My new neighbour has three dogs two of ......... are
    French poodles.
f   Fishing ......... is a popular pastime is very relaxing.
g   My car ......... I have had for over five years needs a
    thorough overhaul.
h   He has three sisters all of ......... are teachers.
i   My youngest child ......... picture I have enclosed is
    learning to play the piano.
j   Our new teacher ......... name I can never remember was
    born in Manchester.


**4** Put the following sentences into Reported Speech:

a   You mustn't tell anybody what I've just told you.
b   Don't begin the lecture until everyone is seated.
c   'Why is she crying?' 'She has failed in the examination.'
d   'Do you know what he is doing here?' 'I have no idea.'
e   'I think it's going to be a wonderful party. Are you going?'
    'I haven't been invited.'
f   'Would you like to come with us?' 'Yes, if I can bring my
    friend.'
g   'Shall I post the letters?' 'You can leave them on the table.
    I'll post them myself.'
h   'What would you do if you were rich?' 'I'd go on a world tour.'
i   Take the dog out for a walk; he needs some exercise.
    'Shall I help you?' 'I'd rather do it myself.'

**5   Clauses of Time.**

Complete the following sentences in any suitable way.

a   I'll be able to pay you as soon as I .........
b   Don't give him any money until he .........
c   I shall prepare dinner while you .........
d   I shall do my shopping after I .........
e   He will do his homework before he .........
f   When I see him, I .........
g   I shall never forget you as long as I .........
h   By the time the others arrive, we .........
i   Don't forget to remind him about it when you .........
j   She ......... while the children are playing in the garden.

**6**   Explain the difference between the two sentences.

a   I am looking forward to his          I am not looking forward to
    visit.                               his visit.
b   I mustn't do it now.                 I needn't do it now.
c   Turn down the radio.                 Turn off the radio.
d   Try to get up early.                 Try getting up early.
e   He has gone to Paris.                He has been to Paris.
f   This is a picture of Sally.          This is a picture of Sally's.
g   If I have time, I'll go.             If I had time I'd go.
h   Have you got enough room?            Have you got enough rooms?


# PAPER 28

**1**   Put the verbs in parentheses into a correct form:

When I (*come*) home last night, my brother already (*go*) to bed,
but my sister still (*do*) her homework. 'I (*work*) for the last two
hours,' she said. 'If I (*not be*) so tired, I (*can*) (*work*) much faster.
I wish I (*begin*) my homework earlier.' When I (*look*) at what she
(*do*) so far, I (*see*) that she (*make*) several mistakes. I (*tell*) her
(*read*) it again very carefully and if she (*not find*) the mistakes, I
(*point*) them out to her. After I (*have*) something (*eat*), she (*show*)
it to me again. I (see) that she (*find*) all the mistakes but one.

66

**2**  Complete the phrasal verbs by putting in the missing particle. Choose from:

*on, out, off, down, up.*

a  I must finish ......... this work before I leave.
b  I was tired ......... when I came home from work.
c  The judge let him ......... with a fine.
d  Would you please sew ......... this button for me.
e  He was bought ......... by one of the big firms.
f  As a result of the popularity of television, many cinemas have had to close .........
g  Will someone please clear ......... this mess?
h  They tried to hush ......... the scandal.
i  I'm afraid that the secret has leaked .........
j  You should polish ......... your English before you leave for London.

**3**  Participial Construction

Complete the following sentences in any suitable way:

EXAMPLES: Feeling rather warm, George took his jacket off.
                   Not being able to get tickets, they went to a café instead.

a  Being a wealthy man, .........
b  Not having any other choice, .........
c  Hearing a knock at the door, .........
d  Not finding anybody at home, .........
e  Finding the conversation boring, .........
f  Wanting to give his children a pleasant surprise, .........
g  Having had a little too much to drink, .........
h  Not wanting to hurt her feelings, .........
i  Having seen the play twice, .........
j  Feeling rather hungry, .........

**4**  Put in the correct tense form of the verb *do* or *make*:

a  What does he ......... for a living?
b  Who is going to ......... the arrangements?
c  It's not so easy to ......... a living these days.
d  It there's no sugar, I can ......... without.
e  Be careful not to ......... any damage.

f   I wouldn't ......... business with him even if I knew it would ......... me rich.

g   I could ......... with a cold drink.

h   A holiday would ......... wonders for you.

i   There's no need to thank me. I was only ......... my duty.

j   I haven't ......... much progress so far.

k   I hope you'll ......... better next time.

l   Have you ......... your homework?

m   I'll ......... my best to avoid ......... mistakes.

n   'Shall I ......... him an offer?' 'Please .........'

o   I ......... the journey in two hours.

**5**   Write questions or statements to which the following could be answers:

| | |
|---|---|
| a   No, I wish I could. | b   The aeroplane is. |
| c   With milk, please. | d   It depends on the weather. |
| e   That's my business. | f   No, thank you. |
| g   Of course I can. | h   I'll take a taxi. |
| i   Only for a few days. | j   It doesn't depend on me. |

**6**   The following words have been omitted from the paragraph. Put them back in the right places:

| | | |
|---|---|---|
| suffers | increased | presumably |
| raised | sensible | proportion |
| while | pace | malnutrition |

It is not very ...... to ask the question: Can the world feed itself? ......... there are people in the world they will ......... be fed. What is more important is the question whether the enormous ......... of the world's population that ......... from ......... can have its standard ......... and whether the world production of food can be ......... in order to keep ......... with the growing population.

# PAPER 29

**1**  Put the verbs in parentheses into a correct form:

a  I wish I (*be*) there now.

b  If I (*know*) last week, I (*make*) different arrangements.

c  It's time we (*go*) home. It (*get*) late.

d  Nobody (*hear*) from him since he (*change*) his job.

e  The telegram (*come*) just as I (*leave*) the house. If it (*come*) five minutes later, I (*not receive*) it.

f  I hope you (*finish*) by the time we (*get*) back.

g  'It (*rain*) now.' 'It (*be*) only a shower. I (*be*) sure that by the time we (*be*) ready to leave, it (*stop*).'

h  That picture (*hang*) in the same place since I (*buy*) it.

i  'I (*like*) (*speak*) to George.' 'I'm sorry but he just (*go*) out.' 'When he (*return*)?' 'I (*have*) no idea.' 'Well, when he (*return*), please (*tell*) him I (*call*).'

j  He is very angry. Seldom I (*see*) him in such a temper.


**2**  Put in the missing prepositions:

a  I met him . . . . . . . . chance.

b  My dress is similar . . . . . . . . yours.

c  He's generous . . . . . . . . his money.

d  It was thoughtful . . . . . . . . you to send . . . . . . . . the doctor.

e  This machine is definitely inferior . . . . . . . . mine.

f  Travelling . . . . . . . . air is preferable . . . . . . . . travelling . . . . . . . . sea.

g  He has been here . . . . . . . . Friday.

h  The job calls . . . . . . . . a sound knowledge . . . . . . . . English.

i  Water consists . . . . . . . . hydrogen and oxygen.

j  I can't dance . . . . . . . . that music.


**3**  Complete the following sentences by using the correct form of the words in parentheses:

a  (*receive*) There was a . . . . . . . . after the wedding ceremony.

b  (*understand*) I'm really very sorry; the whole thing was due to a . . . . . . . .

c   (*help*) John has been very ......... recently.

d   (*sincere*) I don't doubt his .........

e   (*confide*) I should like to speak to you in .........

f   (*contempt*) What a ......... thing to do!

g   (*drama*) He's going to ......... his novel.

h   (*discipline*) We may have to take ......... action.

i   (*appreciate*) They are very ......... of what is being done for them.

j   (*attend*) Please pay ......... to what I am about to say.


**4**  Put the following sentences into the Active Voice. Where necessary the subject of the sentence is given in parentheses:

EXAMPLE: It must be found before we leave. (*John*)

          John must find it before we leave.

a   She never pays any attention to what is said to her. (*people*)

b   The work would have been finished if I had had the time.

c   Billions of dollars are still being spent on armaments. (*Governments*)

d   It used to be thought that the earth was flat. (*people*)

e   The house was being cleaned when I came home. (*my mother*)

f   Quite a number of mistakes have been made. (*the students*)

g   The stolen goods have been found. (*the police*)

h   A great deal of damage was done by the earthquake.

i   It should have been left where it was found. (*You*)

j   When is the house going to be painted? (*they*)


**5**  Idioms for discussion and paraphrase:

a   Pull one's weight.

b   Know one's own mind.

c   Kill time.

d   See eye to eye with someone.

e   Lose heart.

f   Rack one's brains.

g   Red tape.

h   Leave well alone.


**6**  Replace the italicized words with those supplied in parentheses and make any other necessary changes. Do not change the meaning of the sentence:

EXAMPLE: I cannot *make* him do it. (*force*)
      I cannot force him to do it.

a   He *let* me go home early. (*allowed*)
b   He *advised* me to go home early. (*suggested*)
c   I haven't seen him *for* six months. (*since*)
d   *Do* you mind if I bring a friend? (*would*)
e   I met him *while* I was in Paris. (*during*)
f   I *like* to swim in the sea. (*enjoy*)
g   I *told* him I couldn't go. (*said*)
h   *Although* I have read the story twice, I don't understand it. (*nevertheless*)
i   He *told* us the story. (*explained*)
j   The exercise was *so* difficult that nobody could do it. (*such*)
k   We *spoke* about the problem. (*discussed*)
l   He hasn't finished the book *yet*. (*still*)

# PAPER 30

**1**  Put the verbs in parentheses into a correct form:

While I (*drive*) to London last week, I (*stop*) (*give*) a soldier a lift. While we (*speak*) he suddenly (*go*) white and almost (*faint*). I (*take*) him to the nearest hospital, where the doctor on duty (*give*) him a thorough examination but (*cannot*) (*find*) anything wrong with him. After (*give*) him a caffeine injection, the doctor (*tell*) him (*go*) home and (*lie*) down for a few hours. I (*take*) him home and he (*thank*) me very much. He said it must (*be*) something he (*eat*). I (*have*) a letter from him the other day (*tell*) me he (*feel*) fine.

**2**  Complete the phrasal verbs by putting in the missing particle. Choose from:

   *down, up, off, out.*

a   Pull ......... a chair and sit down.
b   The pilot manage to bale ......... in time.
c   When the excitement had finally died ......... the speaker continued as if nothing had happened.

d You are doing very well, Keep it .........

e The banknote turned ......... to be a forgery.

f The musicians tuned ......... their instruments before the performance began.

g The police took ......... their names and addresses.

h I've been trying all the week to shake ......... this cold.

i He is laid ......... with a bad cold.

j Why don't you shave ......... your moustache?

**3** Put in *still* or *yet*:

a 'Have the others finished .........?' 'No, they are ......... working.'

b We ......... haven't heard from John.

c Does he ......... work for that firm?

d You should be glad you are ......... alive.

e We needn't leave .........

f Are the children ......... here?

g Are the children here .........?

h He behaved badly; ........., you should forgive him.

i He worked very hard, ......... he failed in the examination.

j He hasn't ......... had a letter from her.

k 'Isn't he married .........?' 'No, he's ......... a bachelor.'

l This problem is more difficult .........

**4** Rewrite the following sentences in the Causative Form:

EXAMPLES: I told her to dust the room.

I had the room dusted.

I shall tell her to make several copies.

I shall get several copies made.

a I am going to ask them to publish the story.

b I told the man to paint the outside walls.

c He told the man to take his photograph.

d I am going to tell him to renew the contract.

e I must tell her to iron my shirts.

f I shall have to tell her to check the accounts.

g I told the man to clean and press my suit.

h He told the photographer to enlarge the photos.

i I must tell someone to repair the damage.

j Please tell someone to take my bags to my room.

**5** Complete the following sentences in any suitable way:

a The doctor suggested . . . . . . . .
b The doctor advised . . . . . . . .
c The doctor insisted . . . . . . . .
d The doctor urged . . . . . . . .
e The doctor told . . . . . . . .
f The doctor persuaded . . . . . . . . .
g The doctor recommended . . . . . . . . .
h The doctor disapproved of . . . . . . . .
i The doctor wants . . . . . . . .
j The doctor wouldn't allow . . . . . . . .

**6** The following words have been omitted from the paragraph. Put them back in the correct places:

| | | | |
|---|---|---|---|
| draining | Experts | need | weeds |
| results | ditches | sow | grants |
| skilled | improve | piped | fertilizers |

Farmers can always have help from scientists, and they can get all the . . . . . . . . advice they . . . . . . . . . . . . . . . . . . tell them how to destroy . . . . . . . . ., what seeds to . . . . . . . . ., and what . . . . . . . . will give the best . . . . . . . . The Government helps them to . . . . . . . . their farms by making . . . . . . . . of money for . . . . . . . . water-logged fields, clearing . . . . . . . . ., and bringing . . . . . . . . water to the farmstead.

# PAPER 31

**1** Put the verbs in parentheses into a correct form:

Last week I (*invite*) several friends to dinner. When the first couple (*arrive*), I still (*work*) in the kitchen; for I quite (*not finish*) (*prepare*) the salad. I tell them (*make*) themselves at home, (*add*) that I (*join*) them in a few minutes. If they (*come*) ten minutes later, I (*be*) ready for them. The dinner (*be*) an excellent one and I (*compliment*) on my (*cook*). One of my friends (*say*) that he (*go*) (*send*) his wife to me for cooking lessons. I enjoy (*work*) in the kitchen if somebody else (*do*) the washing up.

**2**  Put in the missing prepositions:

a  He was dismissed ......... his job.
b  You shouldn't joke ......... such important matters.
c  He rarely loses ......... cards.
d  What did you mean ......... that remark?
e  He will be a witness ......... the prosecution.
f  Why did you quarrel ......... him ......... such a trivial matter?
g  The car collided ......... a bus.
h  Don't answer ......... him. He can speak ......... himself.
i  I coaxed him ......... going.
j  They vanished ......... sight.

**3**  Put the verbs in parentheses into the correct form. Use either an infinitive or a gerund:

a  I used to (*smoke*) thirty cigarettes a day.
b  I can't get used to (*get*) up early.
c  I am not used to (*speak*) in public.
d  I used to (*live*) in a tiny flat overlooking the sea.
e  He is not used to (*live*) in a city.
f  I used to (*play*) the violin but I haven't done so for years.
g  I must get used to (*speak*) English without translating from French.
h  He used to (*walk*) to work but now he goes by car.
i  Let me do it. I'm used to (*carry*) heavy loads.
j  It took him some time to get used to (*drive*) on the left side of the road.
k  I am not used to (*be*) told what to do.
l  Gerda used to (*make*) mistakes in grammar, but she doesn't do so any more.

**4**  Idioms for discussion and paraphrase:

a  Hold one's tongue.
b  Get even with someone.
c  A tall order.
d  Play second fiddle.
e  Make haste.

74

f   Have fun.
g   Hush something up.
h   Lose one's head.


**5**   Put the verbs in parentheses into a correct tense:

a   She would never have bought the dress if she (*not like*) it.
b   If the weather is good, I (*take*) the dog for a walk.
c   You needn't go if you (*not want*) to.
d   If he told me to do it, I (*have*) to obey him.
e   I can't do it unless I (*have*) the tools.
f   If he should come, please (*let*) me know.
g   If he had worked harder, he (*may pass*) the examination.
h   He wouldn't do it if he (*not like*) it.
i   If you haven't done your homework, the teacher (*be*) very angry.
j   It is now a quarter to four. If he (*not be*) here by 4 o'clock we (*go*) without him.


**6**   Put in *a, an* or *the* where required. Note that in some cases no article is necessary:

a   What ......... terrible weather we've been having recently!
b   Let's go and have ......... drink at ......... pub on ......... corner.
c   He's been in ......... hospital for six weeks.
d   ......... Thames is one of ......... longest rivers in ......... England.
e   She goes to ......... prison once ......... month to visit her husband. He was sent to ......... prison for four years.
f   Henry plays ......... piano, but his brother prefers to play ......... football.
g   I saw him walking along ......... Oxford Street.
h   ......... beauty is only skin deep.
i   ......... girl in ......... blue dress is ......... friend of mine.
j   ......... apples grow in many parts of ......... world, but ......... apples that grow here are ......... best I've ever tasted.

# PAPER 32

**1**  Put the verbs in parentheses into the correct form. Pay attention to word order:

I (*sit*) in my office the other day when I (*tell*) that someone (*want*) (*see*) me. It was Harold Fortiss, an old friend of mine. When I (*ask*) him how he (*be*), he (*tell*) me a rather sad story. He told me that he (*have*) to close down his business because of financial difficulties and that he (*look*) for a job. He (*add*) that if he (*not find*) one quickly, he (*be*) in serious trouble. He (*ask*) me whether I (*can*) (*do*) anything (*help*) him (*find*) something interesting. I (*say*) (*do*) my best and (*ask*) him (*give*) me a ring the following day.

**2**  Complete the phrasal verbs by putting in the missing particle. Choose from:
   *on, off, out, behind, up, about.*

a  John has asked me ......... to dinner.
b  The children spent the afternoon blowing ......... the balloons.
c  We may have to break ......... diplomatic relations with Ruritania.
d  I wonder what brought ......... the quarrel.
e  I really must brush ......... my French.
f  We are going to send ......... our luggage in advance.
g  Attendance at cricket matches falls ......... at the end of the season.
h  If there is one thing I hate, it is filling ......... forms.
i  You go ahead; I'll follow ......... later.
j  I have fallen ......... with my correspondence.

**3**  Complete the following sentences by using the correct form of the words in parentheses:

a  (*critic*) Why are you so ......... of everything I do?
b  (*critic*) Why do you ......... everything I do?
c  (*favour*) I am waiting for a ......... opportunity.
d  (*influence*) He is a very ......... person.
e  (*origin*) You must try to show more .........
f  (*predict*) Most of his ......... have come true.

76

g  (*receive*) See that you get a ......... for the money.
h  (*inherit*) He spent his ......... in less than a year.
i  (*glory*) It's a ......... day for a picnic.
j  (*grammar*) He often makes .......... mistakes.

**4**  Write questions or statements to which the following could be responses:

a  That's all right; I'm not superstitious.
b  No thanks. I'd rather stay at home.
c  It was excellent.
d  The top shelf, please.
e  He's only joking.
f  I'm not surprised.
g  He wouldn't dare.
h  It's up to you.

**5**  Put the following sentences into Direct Speech:

a  She said she was sure she had done well in the test.
b  When I asked her why she wasn't going, she said she had so much work to do that she would have to stay up till midnight to finish it.
c  He asked me where I was going for my holidays, saying he would like to go with me if it was possible.
d  I asked her whether she had answered the letter and she said that she had.
e  He asked me to come back in ten minutes, adding that he would be ready to leave as soon as he had finished what he was doing.
f  He wanted to know what I meant by interrupting him in the middle of his work, and ordered me to get out of his office.

**6**  Write sentences to show the difference between the two words in each of the following pairs:

| affect | spare | childish | earnest | shade |
|--------|-------|----------|---------|-------|
| effect | save | childlike | serious | shadow |

# PAPER 33

**1** Put the verbs in parentheses into a correct form. Use the Passive Voice wherever possible. Pay attention to word order:

a   If more money (*need*), it (*find*). (Three possibilities)
b   It should (*do*) before the foundations (*lay*). Now it's too late.
c   The house (*change*) hands three times since it first (*build*).
d   The dinner still (*cook*) when we (*arrive*); but since the table already (*lay*), we (*tell*) (*seat*).
e   Why I (*not tell*) earlier? I ought (*inform*) immediately.
f   If the letter (*not find*) by tomorrow, he may (*dismiss*).
g   Several people (*interview*) before one finally (*select*).
h   The animals (*feed*) at the same time every morning.
i   The paintings must (*hang*) by an expert. They are really well arranged.
j   It must (*steal*) while the house (*paint*).

**2** Put in the missing prepositions:

a   He took advantage ........ his position.
b   I took it ........ granted that you were going.
c   He is suspected ........ having stolen a car.
d   I was taken ...... surprise.
e   What are you staring ........ ?
f   We all hope ........ a better life.
g   We cannot agree ........ how it should be done.
h   Please write it ........ ink.
i   I have no confidence ........ him.
j   He's independent ........ his family.

**3** Complete the relative clauses in the following sentences. Omit the relative pronoun where it is not already given:

a   The man who ........ will be here next week.
b   War and Peace, which ........, is one of the finest books I have ever read.
c   All ........ is a cup of tea and a sandwich.
d   My niece Jeanette, who ........, has a very good sense of humour.
e   The suit ........ was made in England.
f   The girl whose ........ is very happy.

g That tall man, whose ........., is my neighbour.

h Our neighbour, whom ........., is a very unusual person.

i Bees, which ........., are very industrious creatures.

j The man ........ is an opera singer.

**4** Idioms for class discussion and paraphrase:

a Put one's foot down.

b Have one's hands full.

c Make the most of it.

d To be taken aback.

e Put on airs.

f Pull oneself together.

g Pull wool over someone's eyes.

h Let the cat out of the bag.

**5** Put in *a, an, the* or *some* only where necessary:

a Please put ......... fruit on ......... table.

b He leaves ........ home at 8 o'clock and arrives at ........ school at 8.30.

c I never have ......... coffee after ......... dinner.

d I'd like ......... tea. Would you please make .........?

e I don't like to see ......... house without ......... books.

f ......... Everest is ......... highest mountain in ......... world.

g Most people eat ......... bread with their meals.

h ......... fishmonger at ......... corner of ......... street always has ......... fresh fish.

i Which is ......... more nutritious fruit: ......... apples or ......... oranges?

j I went to ........ Manchester yesterday. On ......... train I met ......... actor and ......... actress ......... actor is quite well known, but ......... actress has only just begun her career.

**6** The following words have been omitted from the paragraph. Put them back in the correct places:

| even | ready-made | weaving |
|------|------------|---------|
| very | articles | afford |
| smart | plentiful | factories |

When machines were invented to do the spinning and ........,
cloth became cheaper and more ........ The sewing machine
was invented in 1851 and ........ soon many ........ of
clothing were being made in ........ Prices dropped and
........ suits and dresses could be bought much more cheaply.
........ those who hadn't much money could now ........,
........, well-fitting clothes.

# PAPER 34

**1** Put the verbs in parentheses into a correct form. Pay attention
to word order:

One day, while I (*wait*) for a bus, someone (*tap*) me on the
shoulder and (*ask*) me if my name (*be*) Alfred. He (*tell*) me that we
once (*work*) in the same office. Although I (*remember*) his name, I
never (*recognize*) him if he (*not speak*) to me. He (*change*) very
much since I last (*see*) him. He told me that he badly (*injure*) in
a road accident and only recently (*come*) out of hospital. On part-
ing, he (*ask*) whether we (*can*) (*meet*) again. I (*take*) his telephone
number and (*say*) that I (*call*) him within the next few days. He
(*say*) he (*look*) forward to (*hear*) from me.

**2** Complete the phrasal verbs by putting in the missing particles.
Choose from:

*out, on, off, in, away, through, up.*

a  I must ring ........ now. I am wanted in the office.
b  Please carry ........ with your work until I return.
c  You'll have to speak ........; those at the back can't hear
   you.
d  Go ........ the contract very carefully before you sign it.
e  Don't let your imagination run ........ with you.
f  Thieves broke ........ during the night.
g  The factory turns ........ five hundred pairs of shoes a day.
h  After a very fierce battle, the enemy finally gave ........
i  I was hungry but the smell from the kitchen put me ........
   my dinner.
j  They are putting ........ a new play at the local theatre.

**3** Complete the following sentences in any suitable way:

a Unfortunately for me, . . . . . . . . .
b Unlike his brother, . . . . . . . . .
c The more he earns, . . . . . . . . .
d He has neither . . . . . . . . . nor . . . . . . . . .
e She spends a lot of money on clothes; however, . . . . . . . . .
f He understood every word I said despite . . . . . . . . .
g He is lazy and careless; consequently . . . . . . . . .
h He is both charming and intelligent, whereas his brother
. . . . . . . . .
i The longer I wait . . . . . . . . .
j I wouldn't help him even if . . . . . . . . .

**4** Rewrite the following sentences using the verb 'have to', making any other necessary changes:
EXAMPLES: Parents are obliged to send their children to school.
Parents have to send their children to school.
Was it necessary for you to leave so early?
Did you have to leave so early?

a If you hadn't come, it would have been necessary for me to take a taxi.
b Were you forced to sell your house?
c Is it necessary for you to work so hard?
d As a result of the strike we were compelled to go on foot.
e It is necessary for him to stay indoors.
f Will he be compelled to resign?
g Is it essential that I should take the examination next week?
h It is essential that you should give up smoking.
i They have been obliged to move to another district.
j Will it be necessary for me to pay cash?
k Will he be forced to resign?
l If he had not apologized, I would have been obliged to dismiss him.

**5** Idioms for discussion and paraphrase:

a The critics picked the play to pieces.
b A short cut.
c It's an open secret.

d   Lend someone a hand.
e   To be at a loose end.
f   To be in a tight corner.
g   To blow one's own trumpet.
h   Call a spade a spade.

**6**  For each word in this list, find another that is pronounced the same but spelt differently: e.g. see, sea; too, two:

| right | blue | vein | eye   | stake  |
|-------|------|------|-------|--------|
| night | pore | week | be    | cruise |

# PAPER 35

**1**  Put the verbs in parentheses into a correct form. Pay attention to word order:

(*Think*) I (*surprise*) my friend, I (*drop*) in on him the other day. He (*sort*) out his collection of postage stamps, something he always (*enjoy*) (*do*). I (*tell*) him that there (*be*) an interesting lecture at the club and (*ask*) him if he (*feel*) like (*go*). When I (*tell*) him who the lecturer (*be*), he (*say*) he very much (*like*) (*go*). He added that he (*hear*) him (*speak*) before and (*be*) very favourably impressed. (*See*) that we (*have*) very little time, we (*take*) a taxi. If we (*not do*) so, we (*be*) late. I (*hate*) (*be*) late for a lecture.

**2**  Put in the missing prepositions:

a   The old man depended ........ his children ........ financial support.
b   He delights ........ playing tricks ........ his friends.
c   He's a disgrace ........ his family.
d   I'm positive ........ it. I saw it ........ my own eyes.
e   Your passport is valid ........ most countries.
f   He's a lawyer ........ profession.
g   They went ........ search ........ adventure.
h   He was inoculated ........ smallpox.
i   I mistook you ........ your sister.
j   Please refrain ........ making a noise.

**3** Complete the following sentences by using the correct form of the words in brackets:

a  (*magnet*) He has a ......... personality.
b  (*boy*) Don't be deceived by his ......... appearance.
c  (*real*) We need a more ......... approach to the problem.
d  (*courage*) Don't be ......... by one failure.
e  (*decide*) Have they reached a ......... yet?
f  (*help*) He stood there ........., not knowing what to do.
g  (*stupid*) I was surprised at his .........
h  (*company*) He ......... me to the station.
i  (*applaud*) The ......... lasted for several minutes.
j  (*grace*) She walks very .........

**4** Explain the difference between the two sentences in each of the following pairs:

a  I'll be there by three o'clock. I'll be there at three o'clock.
b  Walking along the street, I met an old friend. I met an old friend walking along the street.
c  When I came home, the children went to bed. When I came home, the children had gone to bed.
d  I painted the kitchen. I had the kitchen painted.
e  It's rather warm. It's fairly warm.
f  I didn't need to go. I needn't have gone.
g  He has a lot of assistance. He has a lot of assistants.
h  It was a tiring journey. It was a tiresome journey.

**5  Participial Construction (Passive Form)**
Complete the following sentences in any suitable way:
EXAMPLE: John was tired out by the long journey and fell asleep immediately.
John, tired out by the long journey, fell asleep immediately.
Tired out by the long journey, John fell asleep immediately.

a  Encouraged by his steady progress, .........
b  Mr. Smith, ruined by the economic depression, .........
c  Tired of waiting, .........
d  Depressed by her poor progress, .........

e The child, frightened by the sudden appearance of the dog, ..........

f Pleased with her child's school report, ..........

g Refreshed by his afternoon nap, ..........

h Delighted with the success of his invention, ..........

i Hurt by her friend's remarks, ..........

j Mr. Jones, delighted to find his new secretary so efficient, ..........

**6** Write sentences to show the difference between the two words in each of the following pairs:

| fewer | fowl | look | listen | melt | careless |
|-------|------|------|--------|------|----------|
| less | foul | see | hear | dissolve | reckless |

# PAPER 36

**1** Put the words in parentheses into a correct form:

I (*be*) interested in public speaking for a number of years and (*consider*) by my friends (*be*) quite a good speaker. A few days ago, I (*ask*) (*take*) part in a public debate. Several of my friends (*go*) (*be*) there, and I (*look*) forward to an interesting evening. Unfortunately, while I (*drive*) to the club, my car (*break*) down and I (*must*) (*take*) a taxi. I (*arrive*) just as the chairman (*open*) the meeting. I (*make*) my way to the platform and (*apologize*) to the chairman for (*arrive*) late. At the end of the evening I (*tell*) him what (*happen*).

**2** Complete the phrasal verbs by putting in the missing verbs. Pay attention to the tense form. Choose from:

*wear, put, knock, take, help, go, make, leave, find, carry, come, blow.*

a Do you think that benzine will .......... out these stains.

b The blow almost .......... him out.

c I can't .......... out what he is trying to say.

d How can I ..........out who took my book?

e I expect my orders to be .......... out without question.

84

f   This material is so strong it will never ......... out.
g   Could you possibly ......... me out with this problem?
h   Suddenly all the lights ......... out, but they ......... on
    a few minutes later.
i   He ......... out all the candles on the birthday cake.
    Don't forget to ......... my name down. I don't want to be
    ......... out this time.

**3   Idioms for discussion and paraphrase:**

a   Take to one's heels.
b   Take to heart.
c   Take one's time.
d   Split hairs.
e   Mind one's own business.
f   At the eleventh hour.
g   Keep one's distance.
h   A bad debt.

**4   Complete the following sentences in any suitable way:**

a   If the dog hadn't barked, .........
b   If you weren't so tall, .........
c   He wouldn't do it if .........
d   His health will not improve unless .........
e   If my watch hadn't stopped, .........
f   What would you do if .........
g   If I refuse to go, he .........
h   Don't go unless .........
i   If I had a better camera, .........
j   I shall go to the police if .........

**5   Gerund and 'It' as Subjects**
Complete the following sentences and then rewrite each sentence,
beginning with 'It':

EXAMPLES:   Riding a bicycle is easy.
            It is easy to ride a bicycle.
            Learning a foreign language can be very interesting.
            It can be very interesting to learn a foreign language.
            Sending the children alone would be unwise.
            It would be unwise to send the children alone.

85

a Doing homework is ........
b Meeting old friends can be ........
c Driving in wet weather is sometimes ........
d Travelling by ship is generally ........
e Writing letters is usually ........
f Watching children playing is always ........
g Walking long distances is ........
h Teaching children to read can sometimes be ........
i Arguing with obstinate people is ........
j Listening to music is ........
k Swimming in a rough sea can be ........
l Collecting stamps is ........
m Living by oneself is usually ........
n Meeting people from other countries is always ........
o Eating heavy meals before going to bed is ........

**6** The following words have been omitted from the paragraph. Put them back in the correct places:

| | | |
|---|---|---|
| neither | demand | expanding |
| storage | international | development |
| greatly | quantities | determined |

Modern trade, cold .......... and canning have ........ favoured the ........ ... of fruit growing in many parts of the world. The ........ trade in fruit is large and ........, and much of it is ........ by the fact that advanced countries can ........ grow many of the fruits that are in ........ nor grow others in sufficient ........

# PAPER 37

**1** Put the verbs in parentheses into a correct form:

a I (*not see*) John Berry for several months. When I last (*hear*) from him, he (*work*) on a ship. He (*say*) then that he (*get*) in touch with me as soon as he (*return*) to London. I (*like*) (*see*) him again. I always (*enjoy*) (*talk*) to him.

b It's time we (*go*). If we (*not leave*) soon, the family (*wonder*) what (*happen*) to us.

c 'It's a pity you (*not understand*) French. If you (*do*), you (*be*) able (*get*) a much better job than the one you (*have*) now.' 'If I (*think*) it (*help*), I (*start*) (*learn*) tomorrow.'

2 Put in the missing prepositions:

a The book has been translated ........ many languages.
b I heard it ........ the radio.
c He is very good ........ mathematics.
d He was operated ........ yesterday.
e It is not easy to distinguish ........ an American and a Canadian.
f We have not yet arrived ........ a decision.
g ........ the circumstances you'd better stay ........ home.
h The second edition is a great improvement ........ the first.
i His reputation is ........ stake.
j They have struck ........ higher wages.

3 Complete the following sentences by using the correct form of the verbs in brackets:

a (*adjust*) The machine requires one or two minor ........
b (*experiment*) My work is still in the ........ stage.
c (*advise*) It would be ........ to go early.
d (*add*) The work is in ........ to my other duties.
e (*real*) We must stop dreaming and face ........
f (*disaster*) It was a ........ year for business.
g (*cancel*) We've had very few ........
h (*resign*) I cannot accept your ........
i (*enjoy*) It was a very ........ party.
j (*modest*) I think that ........ is a virtue.

4 Complete the following sentences in any suitable way, using Verb + Noun or Pronoun + *to* + Infinitive pattern:
EXAMPLE: The teacher expected the students to do well in the test.

a I advise you to ........
b We cannot force them to ........

87

c We persuaded the children to ........

d She helped me to ........

e I warned him not to ........

f The teacher requested the students to ........

g My sister wants me to ........

h The teacher allowed us to ........

i Can I ask you to ........?

j I didn't expect him to ........

k What tempted him to ........?

l He urged me to ........

m Do you wish us to ........?

n Remind me to ........

o May I trouble you to ........?

**5** Put the following sentences into the Passive Voice. Use 'by' only when you think it is necessary:

a Did the explosion frighten you?

b You should have answered all the questions.

c I must sharpen the knives.

d They sent an invitation to every member.

e Who composed this piece of music?

f We ought to do something about it.

g My brother wrote this poem.

h I wrote the letter in French.

i How often do you water the plants?

j Are you sure that Byron wrote this poem?

**6** Write sentences to show that the following words may be used both as verbs and nouns:

| | | | | |
|---|---|---|---|---|
| book | permit | back | search | leave |
| look | smoke | use | suit | oil |

# PAPER 38

**1** Put the verbs in parentheses into a correct form:

a    When I (*arrive*), he still (*work*). He said that he (*work*) for the last two hours but that he (*go*) (*stop*) in a few minutes. He (*add*) that if I (*arrive*) ten minutes later, I (*may not find*) him at home. When I (*mention*) that the apartment (*look*) rather untidy, he (*say*) that the woman who usually (*clean*) it (*be*) sick for some time and nothing (*do*) for over a week. When I (*ask*) him why he (*not do*) it himself, he (*say*) that he (*intend*) (*do*) so if Mrs. Jones (*not come*) the following day.

b    Now put the conversation into Direct Speech. Begin: He said, 'I have been working .........'

**2** Complete the phrasal verbs by adding the missing particle. Choose from:

     *by, up, in, off, into, out.*

a    'Mr. Jones is waiting to see you.' 'Please show him .........'
b    We can't very well go out until the rain lets ........
c    Some joker has let the air ........ of my tyres.
d    You shouldn't keep the children ......... so late.
e    The garden has been very well laid ........
f    He went ........ business at a very early age.
g    When one is bored, time goes ........ very slowly.
h    I know he's not much to look at, but I wouldn't go ......... appearances if I were you.
i    Meat goes ........ very quickly in hot weather.
j    'You are late.' 'We were held ........ by the fog.'

**3** Idioms for discussion and paraphrase:

a    Beat about the bush.
b    Bite off more than one can chew.
c    Chop and change.
d    Get one's own back.
e    Go the whole hog.
f    Know what's what.
g    Make head or tail of it.
h    Catch alight.

**4** Complete the following sentences in a suitable way, using Verb + Noun or Pronoun + Infinitive (without *to*) pattern:

EXAMPLE: I saw the policeman arrest the man.

a   Please let the children .........
b   It's difficult to make children .........
c   I saw him .........
d   Did you notice the man .........?
e   The porter helped me .........
f   I watched the garage mechanic .........
g   Have you ever heard my daughter .........?
h   I have never known him .........
i   My wife makes me .........
j   She wouldn't let us .........
k   The teacher made the students .........
l   The policeman observed the thief .........
m   Would you please help me .........?
n   Did you see her? .........
o   Did you hear them .........?

**5** Complete the following sentence by adding a relative clause. Do *not* use relative pronouns or commas:

EXAMPLES:   The girl ......... is very attractive.
            The girl you danced with is very attractive.
            The knife ......... seems to be blunt.
            The knife you are using seems to be blunt.

(Note: These are often referred to as *Contact clauses*.)

a   The book ......... is out of print.
b   She is one of the most interesting people .........
c   The stamps ......... are worth quite a lot of money today.
d   The man ......... has finally been caught.
e   The play ......... is excellent.
f   The house ......... is very pretty.
g   The girl ......... has left the country.
h   This is the book .........
i   The shoes ......... are rather tight.
j   The pen ......... has disappeared.

**6** The following words have been omitted from the paragraph. Put them back in the correct places:

90

| foundations | surveyor | area | drains |
| commences | interesting | feet | stage |
| concrete | being | plot | pipes |

It is very ......... to watch a house ......... built. The first
......... is for the ......... to mark out the ......... Then
men come to lay ......... and water ........., make roads and
bring gas and electricity into the ......... Trenches are dug two
or three ......... deep for the ......... of the walls. The
bottom of these trenches is filled with ......... and, when this is
hard, bricklaying .........

# PAPER 39

**1**  Put the verbs in parentheses into a correct form:

While I (*wait*) for a bus the other day, it suddenly (*begin*) (*rain*) I
(*not take*) my umbrella; nor I (*wear*) a coat. While I (*wonder*)
whether or not (*take*) shelter, the bus (*arrive*) and I (*get*) on. I
wonder why it always (*rain*) when I (*leave*) my umbrella at home –
at least, that's how it (*seem*) to me. Fortunately, by the time I
(*reach*) my destination, the rain (*stop*). There are occasions when I
(*enjoy*) (*walk*) in the rain, but I (*like*) (*be*) properly (*dress*) for the
occasion.

**2**  Put in the missing prepositions:

a  This shop specializes ......... clothes ......... young
    people.

b  An officer is responsible ......... his superior ......... the
    men ......... him.

c  The house has been valued ......... ten thousand pounds.

d  There's a bridge ......... the river.

e  You can't prevent him ......... going.

f  I answered all the questions ......... any difficulty.

g  He has left the child ......... good hands.

h  I was ......... the impression that you didn't like him.

i  He prides himself ......... his appearance.

j  'Have you heard ......... John recently?' 'No, not ........
    some time.'

**3** Complete the following sentences by giving the correct form of the words in parentheses:

a  (*progress*) He has very ......... ideas.
b  (*general*) With so few examples you shouldn't .........
c  (*author*) I have ......... him to act on my behalf.
d  (*choose*) I have already made my .........
e  (*coincide*) It was a remarkable .........
f  (*convert*) Dollars are ......... all over the world.
g  (*delinquent*) Juvenile ......... is a serious problem today.
h  (*define*) I want a ......... answer by the end of the week.
i  (*popular, offend*) 'What is the reason for his .........?' 'He seems to take pleasure in using ......... language.'
j  (*surround*) The rooms are nice but I don't like the .........

**4** Complete the following sentences in a suitable way; using Verb + Noun or Pronoun + Present Participle pattern:

EXAMPLES: I watched the children dancing.
Look at that old man working in the garden.

a  Can you hear the dogs .........?
b  If I catch you ........., I shall punish you.
c  When I came home, I found the children .........
d  Fancy him .........!
e  I don't fancy ......... on a night like this.
f  When they forced their way into the house they found the old man .........
g  I heard someone ........., so I went to see who it was.
h  The manager caught him ......... and sent for the police.
i  I didn't notice anybody .........
j  He was so nervous, he could almost hear his heart .........
k  I hear her ......... day and night. She gets on my nerves.
l  I can't imagine her .........
m  Please don't keep me ......... longer than necessary.
n  If I catch you ........., there will be trouble.
o  Did you see him .........?

**5** Idioms for discussion and paraphrase:

a  His bark is worse than his bite.
b  Let the matter drop.

92

c   Make eyes at a person.
d   Run a temperature.
e   It runs in the family.
f   Turn one's head.
g   Call someone names.
h   Call it a day.

**6** Write sentences to show that the following nouns may be countable or uncountable:
light, paper, responsibility, death, marble, adventure.
EXAMPLE: *Light* travels faster than sound. (Uncountable)
I saw a *light* in the room. (Countable)

# PAPER 40

**1** Put the verbs in parentheses into a correct form:

a   I (*work*) at the crossword puzzle for over an hour, but I (*make*) very little progress so far.

b   'As soon as I (*finish*) (*write*) this letter, I (*take*) a walk. I (*not be*) out of the house today. You (*like*) (*join*) me?' 'I (*love*) to. Give me a call as soon as you (*be*) ready (*leave*).'

c   'What he (*do*) when you (*see*) him?' 'He (*sit*) in a corner (*talk*) to John.'

d   'What he (*do*) when he (*see*) you?' 'He (*smile*) and (*raise*) his hat.'

e   'The teacher (*arrive*) yet?' 'No, at least I (*not see*) him.' 'That's strange; he (*never be*) late before.' 'Well, if he (*not come*) today, it (*be*) the first lesson he (*miss*) since the course (*begin*).'

f   'I (*do*) it tomorrow?' 'I'd rather you (*do*) it today.'

**2** Fill in the blank spaces with one of the following groups. Pay attention to the tense form of the verb:

| | | | |
|---|---|---|---|
| back out of | come up to | put up with | do away with |
| look up to | go in for | break in on | fall back on |
| look down on | watch out for | keep up with | make up for |

a  I refuse to ......... his nonsense any longer.
b  How can I ......... the time I have lost?
c  He's a wonderful person to work for. He's ......... by every member of the staff.
d  Do you intend to ......... the competition?
e  Don't walk so fast; I can't ......... you.
f  I hope the book ......... my expectations.
g  There's a sharp bend in the road ......... it.
h  I'm sorry to ......... you like this, but you're wanted on the phone.
i  Such laws should have been ......... a long time ago.
j  You promised to do it. You can't ......... it now.
k  Only a snob would ......... a person who did manual labour.
l  I'm not going to touch my inheritance. It's comforting to know that I shall always have it to .........

## 3  Gerund or Infinitive (Passive Voice)

Put the verb in the correct form, using the gerund or the infinitive in the Passive Voice:

EXAMPLES:  I don't like to be told what to do.
I don't remember being told about it.

a  I would like (*transfer*) to another department.
b  I resent (*speak*) to like that.
c  Nobody enjoys (*reprimand*) by his employer.
d  He doesn't mind (*criticize*) as long as the criticism is constructive.
e  Most of us hate (*deceive*).
f  My children always enjoy (*read*) to.
g  I should love (*take*) to the theatre this evening.
h  Some babies enjoy (*bath*) while others dislike it.
i  The potatoes should (*wash*) before (*peel*).
j  Nobody wants (*wake*) in the middle of the night, but last night it couldn't (*avoid*).

4  Complete the following similes. Choose from the following:

| | | | |
|---|---|---|---|
| ice | church mouse | fox | judge |
| gold | peacock | dust | Solomon |
| honey | lord | bee | mule |

a   as proud as a .........      b   as cunning as a .........
c   as drunk as a .........      d   as sweet as .........
e   as stubborn as a .........   f   as good as .........
g   as busy as a .........       h   as cold as .........
i   as poor as a .........       j   as sober as a .........
k   as dry as .........          l   as wise as .........

**5**   Complete the following sentences in any suitable way:

a   You can come whenever .........
b   Wherever I go, I .........
c   Whoever told you that doesn't .........
d   Whenever I go to their house, they .........
e   Take whichever one ......... but please .........
f   Whatever you do, don't .........
g   However rich he may be, I'm sure .........
h   I always ......... whenever I have nothing better to do.
i   Bring whoever ........., but please don't be late.
j   You must do whatever .........

**6**   The following words have been omitted from the paragraph. Put them back in the correct places:

| | | |
|---|---|---|
| originally | spaces | walking |
| residence | area | railings |
| variety | grounds | outdoor |

In your town there are open ......... where people of all ages can enjoy a ......... of ......... activities, e.g. playing team games, golf, tennis, ........., picnics, etc. If such a park is not just a rectangular ......... surrounded by ......... it may well ......... have been the ......... of a large .........

# PAPER 41

**1**   Put the verbs in parentheses into a correct form. Pay attention to word order:

I (*go*) to see my friend yesterday. Only by (*take*) a taxi I (*get*) there on time. If I (*walk*), I (*be*) late. If I (*be*) late, my friend (*be*) angry.

My watch always (*seem*) (*stop*) at the wrong time. It's time I (*have*) a good watch. If I (*do*), I never (*be*) late. My watch (*not be*) the same since something (*go*) wrong with it last year. If my father (*ask*) me what I want for a birthday present, I (*know*) exactly what (*say*).

**2** Put in the missing prepositions:

a  If you are ever ......... difficulty, don't hesitate to ask ......... my help.
b  His life is ......... danger.
c  Please call ......... your earliest convenience.
d  What he had done remained ......... his conscience.
e  I credited you ......... more intelligence than that.
f  He was found to be unfit ......... military service.
g  There are some people who have never heard ......... Shakespeare.
h  He was robbed ......... his money.
i  He is ......... holiday ......... present.
j  The earth revolves ......... the sun.

**3** Complete the following sentences by using the correct form of the words in parentheses:

a  (*base*) What is the ......... purpose of education?
b  (*suit*) The dress is not ......... for such an occasion.
c  (*occasion*) We hear from him .........
d  (*conscience*) He is a very ......... worker.
e  (*heart*) He gave us a very ......... welcome.
f  (*qualify*) As a result of the accident, he was ......... from driving for two years.
g  (*chemist*) I am going to study .........
h  (*mathematics*) He is one of the best known ......... in the country.
i  (*humble*) ......... is a quality possessed by very few people.
j  (*digest*) He suffers from .........

**4** Ask questions or make statements to which the following could be responses:

a  I know I should, but I'm lazy.
b  I'm going to take a taxi.

c   I borrowed my friend's lawn mower.
d   All right, I'll speak more slowly.
e   I sincerely hope so.
f   No, I wish I had.
g   In the top right-hand drawer.
h   Are you sure? It sounds impossible.
i   Neither of us is.
j   I'm sorry but I'm hard up myself.

## 5   Sequence of Tenses

Complete the following sentences in any suitable way:

EXAMPLES:  I am certain (*that*) he will be there.
               I was certain (*that*) he would be there.
               I know (*that*) John took it.
               I knew (*that*) John had taken it.

a   I am sure (*that*) .........
b   John hoped (*that*) .........
c   I am delighted (*that*) .........
d   None of our friends knew (*that*) .........
e   We were sorry (*that*) .........
f   I hear (*that*) .........
g   I was informed (*that*) .........
h   He tells me (*that*) .........
i   I hope (*that*) .........
j   We were all glad (*that*) .........
k   I suppose (*that*) .........
l   I am convinced (*that*) .........
m   I warned you (*that*) .........
n   Did you know (*that*) .........?
o   He promised us (*that*) .........

## 6   Write sentences to show the difference between the two words in each of the following pairs:

| economic | loose | pill | flower | hard |
|---|---|---|---|---|
| economical | lose | peel | flour | hardly |

# PAPER 42

**1** Put the verbs in parentheses into a correct form:

I (*go*) (*see*) my friend yesterday as we previously (*arrange*); for we (*have*) several important things (*discuss*). However, he (*not be*) there when I (*arrive*); nor (*be*) there any message for me. But (*know*) him as I do, I (*be*) sure there (*be*) a good reason for his absence. When he finally (*turn*) up, I (*wait*) more than an hour. He (*say*) that he (*have*) a puncture on the way and (*telephone*) the garage (*ask*) them (*send*) someone (*change*) the wheel. When I (*ask*) him why he (*not do*) it himself, he (*say*) he never (*do*) such a thing before and that he (*have*) no intention of (*start*) now.

**2** Complete the phrasal verbs by putting in the missing particle: Choose from:

*out, off, for, across, on, up, down.*

a   I ran ......... an old friend last week.

b   'Can you take me there?' 'Yes I'll call ........' you at eight o'clock. Please be ready.'

c   I tried ......... several dresses before I found one that suited me.

d   These letters must be sent ......... at once.

e   'I will not stand ......... unpunctuality,' said the manager.

f   Marking homework takes ......... a great deal of time.

g   I worked ......... a system which saved a lot of money.

h   Why do you run him ......... behind his back? You would never dare speak like that if he were here.

i   Throw ......... everything we don't need.

j   We are setting ......... on our trip at seven o'clock in the morning.

**3** Put in *a, an, the* or *some* only where necessary:

a   ......... high cost of ......... living is ......... very serious problem.

b   Why should ......... man retire at ......... age of sixty-five?

c   Have you ever seen such ......... beautiful sunset?

d ........ postman told me there were ........ parcels for me at ........ post-office.

e I have ........ tape recorder, ........ record-player and ........ records; yet I spend most of ........ evening watching ........ television.

f Please go to ........ grocer's and pick up ........ things I ordered.

g 'Who is ........ girl in ........ blue dress?' 'She's ........ new student I was telling you about.' 'She has ........ interesting accent.'

h ........ people are of ........ opinion that ........ rich should help ........ poor.

i Give the child ........ orange. There are ........ on ........ table in ........ other room.

j My mother makes ........ jam from ........ plums that grow in ........ garden.

k He gave me ........ lift to ........ station.

l My mother went to ........ school yesterday to speak to ........ headmaster.

**4** Complete the following sentences in any suitable way:

a If she were here now, she ........

b If you have any complaints, please ........

c If you had done what I told you, you ........

d Unless the rent is paid by the end of the month, ........

e If there isn't enough food, we ........

f We shall never finish the work on time if we ........

g I would have accepted his offer if ........

h If you were not so careless, you ........

i Unless we leave immediately, we ........

j I would do it myself if ........

**5** *Else* Forms

Use the following expressions in sentences of your own:

| | | | |
|---|---|---|---|
| something else | somebody else | somewhere else | Who else? |
| anything else | anybody else | anywhere else | What else? |
| nothing else | nobody else | nowhere else | Where else? |
| everything else | everybody else | everywhere else | When else? |

EXAMPLE: (*When else*) 'Why did you go on Friday?' '*When else* could I go?'

99

**6** The following words have been omitted from the paragraph. Put them back in the correct places:

| | | | |
|---|---|---|---|
| force | apart | sought | overcome |
| natural | upon | unless | especially |
| peaceful | less | barrier | boundaries |

A ......... world is not possible ......... the boundaries between one country and another have been agreed ........., and many countries, ......... the ......... powerful ones, have ......... limits that would at once mark off their territory and be defensible against attack. Frontiers or ......... which afford ......... protection are not easy to find, ......... from the sea, and even this ......... can be ......... by the use of superior naval .........

# PAPER 43

**1** Put the verbs in parentheses into a correct form:

George (*return*) from England last week and tomorrow evening we (*have*) a party (*celebrate*) his return. When you (*see*) him tomorrow, you (*be*) amazed (*see*) how much he (*change*) since we last (*see*) him. When I (*ask*) him what he (*intend*) (*do*) he (*say*) he (*not make*) up his mind yet, but if he (*offer*) a good job he probably (*take*) it and (*start*) (*work*) immediately. He (*add*) that he (*may*) even open a business of his own. However, (*know*) George as I do, I (*think*) he (*be*) far happier (*work*) for somebody else.

**2** Put in the missing prepositions:

a   You must comply ......... the regulations.
b   You should be more tolerant ......... other people's opinions.
c   How will she react ......... the news?
d   Once ......... a while I fall asleep ......... the lesson.
e   We are all ......... favour ......... sending a donation.
f   He left ......... telling anybody. That's typical .........
   him.
g   We must keep ......... touch ......... each other.

h It sounds all right ........ theory but will it work out
........ practice?

i Refreshments will be served ........ the end ........ the
meeting.

j He is held ........ high esteem ........ everybody.


**3** Complete the following sentences by using the correct form of
the words in parentheses:

a (*separate*) They are very close friends; in fact they are
........

b (*compel*) Education is ........ in most countries.

c (*repel*) I dislike him intensely. His manners are ........

d (*wit*) I enjoy his company; he is a very ........ person.

e (*fortune*) ........, he came late and missed the train.

f (*excellent*) He ........ at mathematics.

g (*read*) His handwriting is very bad. It's almost ........

h (*complain*) If you have any ........ to make, please speak
to the manager.

i (*determine*) He is still ........ whether or not to go.


**4** Join the following pairs of sentences by making the second in
each pair into a non-defining relative clause. In this exercise the
relative pronoun cannot be omitted. All the sentences require
commas:

EXAMPLE: George and Mary are getting married next week.
They are coming for dinner tonight.
George and Mary, who are coming for dinner tonight,
are getting married next week.

a My eldest son has just returned from the United States. His
new novel was published last month.

b Chess is quite a difficult game. More and more people are
learning to play it.

c My mother-in-law is coming to spend a week with us. I enjoy
her company very much.

d These exercises are good for us. We do them every day.

e My Uncle George is very upset about it. His car was badly
damaged in an accident.

f My niece is only five years old. She can read and write English.

101

g My father advises me to study medicine. I have great confidence in his judgement.

h Our French teacher is devoted to his work. We enjoy his lessons very much.

i My friend has an excellent collection of postage stamps. He is a very keen philatelist.

j He has five children. They all went to the same school.

**5** Put the following sentences into Direct Speech. Pay attention to the punctuation:

a Henry said that the new machine had just arrived and asked where he should put it. I told him to leave it where it was for the time being, saying that I would tell him later what to do with it.

b He asked us who we were and how we had got into the building. We told him we were newspaper reporters and that we wanted to know something about the robbery that had taken place the previous night. He said that we had no right to be there and added that if we didn't leave immediately, he would call the police.

c When she said she didn't like the seats, I told her not to complain and added that we were lucky to have got seats at all.

d I asked the manager whether I could pay my bill that night, explaining that I had to leave very early the following morning. He said he would prepare the account and asked what time I would like to be called.

**6** Write sentences to show that the following words may be used both as verbs and nouns:

| | | | | |
|---|---|---|---|---|
| touch | rain | cook | walk | risk |
| fight | snow | drink | result | dive |

EXAMPLE: It was a very graceful *dive*. (Noun)
He *dived* into the water. (Verb)

# PAPER 44

**1** Put the verbs in parentheses into a correct form:

a I (*not go*) (*wait*) for Frank. By the time he (*be*) ready, it (*be*) too late (*go*) anywhere.

b We (*stand*) at the bus-stop for about ten minutes when a passer-by (*tell*) us that the last bus already (*go*). It seems strange that in a city like London buses (*stop*) (*run*) so early.

c John (*come*) to work late recently. The manager already (*speak*) to him. If he (*not be*) careful, he (*may*) (*find*) himself out of a job.

d As he (*run*) (*catch*) the bus, he (*fall*) and (*break*) his leg. He (*be*) in hospital for over a week, but (*expect*) (*be*) out tomorrow.

e 'This is the third time you (*fall*) asleep while (*work*). (*Be*) anything the matter?' 'We (*have*) some trouble with the baby recently I think he's teething. I hardly (*close*) my eyes last night.'

f (*Guess*) who I (*find*) (*wait*) for me when I (*get*) home.

**2** Complete the following sentences by adding the missing particle. Choose from:
*over, off, on, out, away, up, down.*

a I have a slight headache but I am sure it will pass . . . . . . . .

b My grandmother passed . . . . . . . . last week.

c Business is picking . . . . . . . . ; the firm has taken . . . . . . . . ten new workers.

d I'd appreciate your help, but please don't put yourself . . . . . . . .

e Slow . . . . . . . . before you get to the traffic lights.

f He's never been so well . . . . . . . . in his life.

g It was quite a shock but she'll get . . . . . . . . it.

h It's time you got married and settled . . . . . . . .

i When the news gets . . . . . . . . , there's going to be trouble.

j 'How did you get . . . . . . . . in the examination?' 'I'm sure I passed it.'

**3** Idioms for discussion and paraphrase:

a Make ends meet.

b Keep something dark.

c Take advantage of something or someone.
d Keep a straight face.
e Keep up appearances.
f Keep one's temper.
g The chance of a lifetime.
h A going concern.

## 4 Unreal Past (Wish)

EXAMPLES: It's a pity they aren't here. = I wish they were here.
I'm sorry I wasn't there. = I wish I had been there.
It's a pity I didn't tell him. = I wish I had told him.

Now put the verbs in parentheses into the correct tense:

a I wish I (*not invite*) him.
b I wish the other students (*be*) here now.
c I wish I (*not begin*) this work.
d I wish she (*not talk*) so much.
e It's time you (*have*) a car.
f I wish I (*have*) a good memory.
g I wish I (*be*) more careful when I did the homework.
h Suppose he (*ask*) you to marry him. What would you do?
i If only there (*be*) peace in the world!
j I wish I (*not sell*) my car.

## 5 'Should Have Done', 'Ought to Have Done'
Study the following conversation:

John: 'I went by bus and arrived late.'
Bill: 'You shouldn't have gone by bus; you should have taken a taxi.'

Now reply to the following statements in a similar way:

a I drank some coffee and, as a result, I slept badly.
b I took the child to the theatre but he didn't enjoy it.
c I spoke to him in French, but he couldn't understand me.
d I wrote the composition quickly and made several mistakes.
e I bought a cheap shirt, but after a month I could not wear it any longer.
f I sent the child alone and he got lost.
g I sat at the back and could hardly hear a word.
h She kept her money under the bed and one day she was robbed of every penny she had.

She wore a cotton dress, but it was rather chilly and she caught a cold.

j She washed her sweater in hot water and it shrank.

Now repeat the exercise, using *ought to* instead of *should*.

**6** The following words have been omitted from the paragraph. Put them back in the correct places:

| | | |
|---|---|---|
| insignificant | seeds | involved |
| communities | apart | cultivation |
| fundamental | animal | variety |

Man obtains his basic necessity, food, in a ......... of ways. Both vegetable and ......... foods are ........., but Man's main dependence is upon vegetable foods which, ......... from the ......... collection of fruits, berries, and ......... by small primitive ........., are obtained through that ......... and almost world-wide occupation known as .........

# PAPER 45

**1** Put the verbs in parentheses into a correct form:

a When I (*finish*) (*read*) this story, it (*be*) the sixth time I (*read*) it.

b When I (*see*) him, he (*read*) the letter the committee (*send*) him. Seldom I (*see*) him so happy.

c When I (*arrive*) at the airport, several other members of the family (*wait*) there. Some of them (*be*) there for quite a time. They all (*come*) (*greet*) our grandfather, who (*not visit*) England for over twenty years.

d If only I (*know*) earlier that you (*go*) (*buy*) a washing machine, I (*can save*) you quite a bit of money. You really should (*mention*) it sooner.

**2** Put in the missing prepositions:

a We cannot remain isolated ......... the rest of the world.

b It's ......... our own interest to insure ......... fire.

c  What do you infer ........ his remarks?
d  I am greatly indebted ........ you ........ your help.
e  There has been an increase ........ the number ........
   road accidents.
f  Don't interfere ........ things that don't concern you.
g  There was someone inquiring ........ you.
h  What are you hinting ........?
i  You've got nothing to grumble ........
j  He gave a party ........ honour ........ his daughter.


3  Complete the following sentences by giving the correct form
of the words in parentheses:

a  (*resist*) They tried to break down the enemy's ........
b  (*persist*) He has ........ attacks of malaria.
c  (*modern*) We must ........ our methods.
d  (*marry*) She's of ........ age.
e  (*deceive*) I wouldn't trust such a ........ person.
f  (*intention*) 'Did he do that ........?' 'No it was quite
   ........,'
g  (*athlete*) He's quite an ........ looking person.
h  (*scarce*) The ........ of a commodity always results in
   higher prices.
i  (*fertile, produce*) We must ........ the soil to make it more
   ........
j  (*success*) I have been here on four ........ days.


## 4  Adjectives and Adverbs (Comparison)
Put the words in parentheses into the correct form of adjective or
adverb:
EXAMPLES:  He speaks (*careful*) than you do.
           He speaks *more carefully* than you do.
           John is (*diligent*) student in the class.
           John is the *most diligent* student in the class.
           The exercise is not (*difficult*) as the first one.
           The exercise is not *as difficult as* the first one.

a  She is (*beautiful*) child I have ever seen.
b  I wish I could speak English (*good*) as John.
c  Your handwriting is much (*good*) than mine.

106

d  Why does he always talk so (*serious*)?
e  I am now working much (*hard*) than I did last year.
f  Mary was (*calm*) student in the class.
g  Today I arrived (*early*) than I did yesterday.
h  This is (*bad*) composition I have ever written.
i  He is one of (*interest*) people I have ever met.
j  He speaks (*confident*) than the other students.
k  His condition today is (*bad*) than it was yesterday.
l  You'll have to be (*careful*) than this if you want to do well in the examination.
m  She doesn't speak (*good*) as her friend, but her written work is much (*good*).
n  Ruth is (*old*) of the two sisters.
o  Flying is (*fast*) and (*convenient*) way of travelling.

## 5  Gerunds following Prepositions

Complete the following sentences in any suitable way, using a gerund after the preposition:

EXAMPLES: He is clever at imitating famous people.
　　　　　He is capable of doing excellent work.

a  You should read the story carefully before ........
b  The teacher began the lesson by ........
c  I never go to bed without ........
d  Can't you eat your soup without ........
e  He thanked me for ........
f  He succeeded in ........
g  You will succeed only by ........
h  He apologized for ........
i  He is not used to ........
j  He made a lot of money by ........
k  I have no intention of ........
l  I am really sorry for ........

## 6  Write sentences to show that the following nouns may be countable or uncountable:

　　*stone　　speech　　chocolate　　experience　　pleasure　　loss*

# PAPER 46

**1** Put the verbs in parentheses into a correct form:

a  If we (*not leave*) soon, we (*arrive*) after the show (*begin*). (*See*) that we are guests, our host (*be*) very angry if we (*do*) such a thing.

b. By the time we (*arrive*), most of the people (*leave*). It (*be*) better if we (*not go*) at all.

c  'You ought (*tell*) me earlier.' 'I'm sorry I (*not do*) so, but it (*not occur*) to me that you (*be*) interested in (listen) to chamber music.'

d  She (*not do*) a stroke of work since she (*leave*) school.

e  (*See*) that there (*be*) nobody at home, I put a note in his letter-box (*tell*) him where I (*intend*) (*spend*) the evening.

f  He (*speak*) for over an hour. If he (*not stop*) soon, he (*talk*) to an empty hall. Several people already (*leave*), and the others (*get*) fidgety.

**2** Fill in the blank spaces with one of the following groups. Pay attention to the tense form of the verb:

| | | | |
|---|---|---|---|
| get out of | stand up for | put in for | mix up in |
| cut out for | come in for | get on for | wait up for |
| look out on | settle up with | lead up to | fall in with |

a  'If you don't ........ your rights, you will be exploited,' said the speaker.

b  He's not ........ that kind of work.

c  Will you please pay the bill? I'll ........ you later.

d  My bedroom ........ a charming little park.

e  The Prime Minister has ........ a great deal of criticism recently.

f  Now I can see what the speaker is ........

g  I've promised to go. I wish I could ........ it.

h  'How old is he?' 'He must be ........ for forty.'

i  We are going to ........ a wage increase.

j  I don't want to get ........ the affair.

k  I'm ready to ........ any proposal you'd like to make.

l  Don't ........ me, Mother. I shall be home very late.

**3** Put the following sentences into the Passive Voice:

a Why did you have to tell him?

b Did the noise disturb you?

c We might increase production if we raised the workers' salaries.

d I would like someone to take me to the theatre.

e They operated on him yesterday.

f They say he is a very generous person.

g I don't want anyone to make a fool of me.

h Someone has deliberately disconnected the telephone.

i You'll have to do it some day.

j He likes people to make a fuss of him.

**4** Idioms for discussion and paraphrase:

a It serves him right.

b To be at a loose end.

c A storm in a teacup.

d To stagger holidays.

e Turn a blind eye.

f Fall on one's feet.

g Jack of all trades.

h At the eleventh hour.

**5** Put in the correct tense form of the verb *do* or *make*:

a You must ......... every effort to be punctual.

b See that all the beds are ......... before you leave.

c He ......... me a good turn when I was in trouble.

d That photograph doesn't ......... you justice.

e Have you ......... all the exercises?

f A person who is superstitious is often afraid to ......... a will.

g I've got two or three telephone calls to .........

h What he says doesn't ......... sense.

i Would you ......... me a favour? I'd like you to ......... a speech tomorrow.

j There's very little food in the house. We'll have to ......... ......... with tinned fish.

k He ......... a very good impression on most people.

l When I saw her, she was ......... her hair.

**6** The following words have been omitted from the paragraph. Put them back in the correct places:

| | | | |
|---|---|---|---|
| healthier | consulted | campaign | reduction |
| increases | conditions | leisure | members |
| strong | means | deal | improve |

The trade unions have done much to ........ the working ........ of millions of men, women and children. By their successful ........ for a ........ in working hours and ........ in wages, they have given working people more ........, and the ........ to enjoy it. They have helped to make factories and mines ........ and safer. They are ........ enough to see that each of their ........ is given a fair ........, and when difficulties arise they are always :........

# PAPER 47

**1** Put the verbs in parentheses into a correct form:

I (*run*) all the way to the station only (*find*) that the train already (*leave*). I (*tell*) that there (*be*) another one in twenty minutes. (*See*) that I (*have*) some time (*spare*), I (*go*) to the news-stand (*buy*) a newspaper. While I (*glance*) through it, I (*hear*) someone (*call*) my name. It (*be*) my friend Alfred, who I (*think*) (*catch*) the earlier train. He, too, (*miss*) it. He (*say*) that he (*catch*) it if his watch (*not be*) slow.

**2** Put in the missing prepositions:

a  We marvelled ........ their audacity.
b  Such remarks are uncalled ........
c  The decision doesn't rest ........ me.
d  He is held ........ high esteem ........ everybody.
e  I wouldn't dream ........ doing such a thing ........ public.
f  All school fees must be paid ........ advance.
g  Don't worry ........ me. I'll be there ........ fail.
h  I can't live ........ such a low salary.

i He lives ......... his wits.
j He's not equipped ......... such a task.
k Two of the soldiers died ......... their wounds.
l He is devoted ......... his wife and children.

**3** Complete the following sentences by putting in the correct form of the words in brackets:

a (*origin*) How did the trouble .........?
b (*apply*) Is the rule ......... in this case?
c (*bitter*) His recent failures have ......... him.
d (*fatal*) He was ......... wounded.
e (*despise*) His behavour was .........
f (*publish, offend*) The ......... of such material may be an ........... against the law.
g (*voluntary*) He ......... for the job although we didn't ask for .........
h (*eternal*) It seemed an ......... before news finally reached us.
i (*qualify*) I'm sure he has the necessary .........
j (*vacant*) There is a ......... for a good secretary.

**4** Complete the following sentences in any suitable way:

a I wish I .........
b Owing to the bad weather, .........
c Whoever said that .........
d ......... unless I say so.
e Neither of the children .........
f It's about time you had the curtains .........
g The doctor said I wasn't to ......... until .........
h He speaks French as if .........
i I am not used to .........
j What are you doing here? Aren't you supposed to .........?
k Do you mind my .........?
l Did you manage to .........?

**5 'Out of'**
Complete the sentences with one of the following words:

breath    sight    date    order    practice
season    print    doors    danger    work

a  I've tried very hard to get the book, but it seems to be out of
   .........
b  That time-table is out of .........
c  Tomatoes are expensive because they are out of .........
d  I waited until the plane was out of ......... and then went
   home.
e  He ran all the way and arrived out of .........
f  Her husband has been out of ......... for six weeks.
g  I used to play table-tennis very well, but I am out of .........
h  I really should spend more time out of .........
i  The doctor says that the patient is now out of .........
j  Since the lift was out of ........., we had to use the stairs.

6  Write sentences to show the difference between the two words
   or phrases in each of the following pairs:

   already    anyone    altogether     anyway     everyday
   all ready  any one   all together   any way    every day


# PAPER 48

1  Put the verbs in parentheses into a correct form. Pay attention
to word order:

a  'What time John generally (*arrive*)?' He generally (*arrive*) at
   about nine o'clock, but he (*telephone*) a few minutes ago (*say*)
   that he (*not be*) at the office before 11 o'clock this morning.'
   'You (*mind*) (*ask*) him (*get*) in touch with me as soon as he
   (*arrive*)?'
b  I wish I (*be*) there when she told him what she (*think*) of him.
   I would like (*see*) his face.
c  We (*need not take*) our raincoats. It didn't rain after all.
d  'You (*like*) (*go*) somewhere this evening?' 'I just as soon (*stay*)
   at home.'
e  She (*work*) for me ever since she (*leave*) school.
f  At the end of this week I (*work*) here exactly four years.
g  If you (*not behave*) yourself, we (*not take*) you with us to the
   circus tomorrow.

112

h She never (*go*) to the party if, she (*know*) that John (*go*) (*be*) there. She (*not see*) him or (*speak*) to him since their engagement (*break*) off. Fortunately, he left very early and so an embarrassing situation (*avoid*).

i My neighbours (*not stop*) (*complain*) ever since my daughter (*start*) (*take*) piano lessons.

j Why you (*not tell*) you (*not finish*) the book? I (*not take*) it back to the library.

**2** Complete the phrasal verbs by adding the missing particle. Choose from:

*out, into, down, up, through, off.*

a Several of the old houses in this street are going to be pulled .........

b I am happy to say that business is looking ........

c Thieves broke ........ the house while we were on holiday.

d The play didn't go ........ as well as we thought it would.

e Would you please make ........ a list of the things we need.

f If the boy who broke the window doesn't own ........., I shall punish all of you.

g The stupid man ran ........ his inheritance in less than a year.

h We have run ........ unexpected difficulties.

i I had a bit of a headache but I managed to sleep it ........

j He wound ........ his speech by saying the struggle would continue until success was assured.

**3** **Gerund or Infinitive**

Put the verbs in parentheses into the correct form, Gerund or Infinitive. Some of the sentences require prepositions. Put them in where necessary.

EXAMPLE: I apologize (*come*) late.
I apologize for coming late.

a He suggested (*go*) to Paris, but we finally decided (*go*) to Rome.

b I'm not interested (*watch*) other people (*dance*), although I enjoy (*dance*) myself.

113

c    She has no intention (*go*) abroad. She intends (*stay*) at home.

d    'Don't let him (*go*) alone,' 'I can't prevent him (*do*) so.'

e    He insisted (*make*) a speech. I didn't want (*risk*) (*offend*) him (*not allow*) him (*do*) so.

f    Although his teacher encouraged him (*continue*) (*paint*), his parents thought this (*be*) a waste of time and tried (*discourage*) him (*do*) so.

g    I have very little opportunity (*speak*) English. I am thinking (*invite*) an English person (*spend*) a month at our home in Granada. Can you help me (*find*) a suitable person?

h    He has been talking for months (*go*) abroad.

i    He accused her (*be*) a snob. I don't think he is justified (*make*) such an accusation.

j    He was reprimanded (*come*) late.


**4**  Rewrite the following sentences making the defining clauses non-defining. Every new sentence requires commas and a relative pronoun:

EXAMPLES:  The dress *I wore last night* is a little too long.

        This blue dress, *which I wore last night*, is a little too long.

        The boy *you were speaking to* just now wants to take me out.

        Harold Marvell, *to whom you were speaking* just now, wants to take me out.


a    The street I live in is a very quiet one.

b    The people I have been staying with for the last two weeks are very charming.

c    The dictionary I received as a birthday present is an excellent one.

d    The museum we are going to visit tomorrow is not very far from here.

e    The person you've been wanting to meet for some time will be here tomorrow.

f    The newspaper I read every morning has an excellent political cartoonist.

g    The boy you met at my house last week is going to marry my sister.

h    The person who wrote this article is an excellent journalist.

114

i The person whose book you borrowed would like you to return it.

j The flowers she sent me on my birthday are still fresh.

## 5 Prefixes and Suffixes

a Write the opposite of the following words by adding a prefix:

| | | | |
|---|---|---|---|
| logical | rational | legal | satisfactory |
| practical | flexible | valid | English |
| continue | pure | ordinary | to like |
| moral | efficient | professional | to be like |

b Form abstract nouns by adding suffixes to the following words:

| | | | | |
|---|---|---|---|---|
| just | snob | refuse | depend | oblige |
| judge | human | know | ignore | realise |
| boy | cynic | humid | partner | enthuse |
| repent | slave | peculiar | jealous | expand |

6 The following words have been omitted from the paragraph. Put them back in the correct places:

| | | | |
|---|---|---|---|
| purposes | vast | deliberately | fuel |
| considerable | over | timber | demand |
| resources | pulp | fraction | pasture |

.......... much of the world today only a small ......... of the original forest remains. A great deal has been ......... removed to provide land for cultivation or ........., while much has been cut down for ........., for building, and for many other .......... In the modern world, the large ......... for softwood for constructional work, pit-props, and ......... and paper, and the smaller yet ......... demand for ......... for furniture and other purposes has led to ......... inroads being made into the world's timber .........